High Tech Product Launch

Second Edition

High Tech Product Launch

Second Edition

Catherine Kitcho

Pele Publications

1833 Limetree Lane

Mountain View, CA 94040

Visit our website at: http://www.pelepubs.com

Printed in the United States of America

Publisher's Cataloging-in-Publication
(Provided by Quality Books, Inc.)

Kitcho, Catherine.

    High tech product launch / Catherine Kitcho. — 2nd ed.

       p. cm.

      Includes index.

      LCCN 2005902086

      ISBN-13: 978-1-929936-04-5

      ISBN-10: 1-929936-04-4

      1. New products—Management. 2. High technology industries—Management. I. Title.

HF5415.153.K55 2005   658.8

          QBI05-200086

Table of Contents

PART II: Market Strategy and Programs

PART III: Launch Planning and Implementation

Going Forward

Introduction to the Second Edition

A time of change

Since I wrote the first edition of High Tech Product Launch in 1998, the U.S. economy and the high tech world in particular have undergone tremendous fluctuations. The high tech boom of the late 1990s became a sudden and dramatic high tech bust by the end of 2000. Startups and established companies went out of business or filed for bankruptcy. Entrepreneurs seeking venture capital were turned away. The U.S. economy experienced a general downturn beginning in 2000, with tremendous job losses, growing deficits, and general shareholder distrust resulting from corporate scandals. Revenues dropped, profits were squeezed, and companies were forced to make drastic cuts to survive. Companies started streamlining their operations and shifting jobs offshore to reduce expenses. The last seven years have been a time of painful changes for business. As a result, the surviving companies have had to make many changes to their companies, processes, and marketing practices.

And some good news

During the last seven years, we have also witnessed dramatic changes in technology that provide us with more efficient tools to market and launch our products. The adoption of Internet technologies and broadband communications have made it possible for any company to do business online around the clock and around the globe. Web hosting has become so inexpensive that even individuals can afford to have their own website. Market research can be entirely done online and much more information has been made available at low prices or for free. Printing of marketing materials is rarely done these days, reserved only for face-to-face communications with customers.

Impact on launch

What impact do all of these changes have on product launch? We have all learned how to make do with less, we have leveraged new technologies and modes of communications, and we have evolved the entire launch process – for the better.

More than ever, launches have become a more central part of a company's business operations. Cross-functional involvement in launch is growing as organizations realize the importance of executing a successful product launch. It can make all the difference in competitive position, and more importantly, sales.

Marketing budgets now receive more scrutiny, so launch expenditures must be justified in terms of overall return on investment. Marketing professionals are putting more effort into planning and budgeting. Companies are beginning to err on the side of simplicity and value in their marketing campaigns. We are leveraging the Internet and company websites to deploy marketing campaigns, saving money and freeing up creative resources to design materials for online venues.

Launch has become more process-oriented, with many companies beginning to document and adopt repeatable launch processes. This saves money and time because a new launch team doesn't have to start from square one each time a new launch needs to be implemented. Even marketing materials that are used for every launch are made into templates for easy updating to fit the next product.

A marriage of marketing and project management

The work of launch has evolved as well. No longer is the launch team a haphazard group of people quickly brought together to execute a launch. Companies are recognizing that the right skills are needed for launch activities. I believe that the practice of product launch is a combination of marketing and project management. Successful launches require the creative and analytical skills of marketing to develop the right programs and strategy. Project management is then applied to the planning and implementation phase of the launch, for managing the deliverables, the people, the schedule and the budget.

Best practices

In the first edition of this book, I stated that when it comes to launches " there was a lot to know and a lot to do. Much of what I now know about product launch I learned the hard way, by trial and error." That's still true. Even after ten years of working with clients, I continue to learn from experience and evolve my launch practices. I've added content to the book that reflects my greater understanding of how to plan and implement launches within an organization of any size. I've found ways to maintain my personal approach to launch: keeping things simple and realistic. In this second edition of the book, I share these best practices with you.

Launching a new product can be fun, frustrating, and very demanding. It takes the combined efforts of many people inside and outside an organization to make it happen. Everyone in the company wants the launch to be a success, and they want to get the product out to market as soon as possible. They want it to be perfectly positioned, so that revenues will begin immediately and they can begin to receive the return on their investment of time, effort, and dollars.

Product launches are rarely perfect. That's because market conditions are constantly changing and customers are fickle.

During the launch, you need to put a stake in the ground that says, "Here is our target market and we will aim for it." But that little spot in the ground doesn't stand still - even for the three to five months during which your product is launched. Other companies like yours also notice that little spot in the ground, and decide that they'd like to go there too. And when you have arrived at your little spot, you find that an earthquake has changed the little spot on the ground, and not only that, you suddenly have lots of company. You hope that you have brought enough weapons and supplies with you to make camp and defend your spot. That is the challenge of product launch.

There is tremendous pressure on the whole company during this period, especially on the launch team. Everyone worries. What if you really blow it, and you spend all this money coming up with marketing materials, and no one buys the product? What if you bomb while out on the press tour, and the press has nothing good to say about your product or your company?

The whole process is filled with risk. All you can do is arm yourself with the best information that is available at the time and a plan for getting to market in a timely fashion. At the end of the day, it's all a matter of luck and timing. The only thing you can do to improve your odds is to do your homework and work diligently toward the goal.

Managing the launch implementation process is stressful. I can recall many times when I was tearing my hair out at the end of the day, thinking that the whole thing was hopeless. But then I'd wake up the next morning, think of some other way to approach the problem, and go at it again. There were other times when it seemed that it wasn't a productive day unless somebody on the launch team was angry with me about something. Somehow you get through it. The process may not be pretty, but the end result is very satisfying, especially when you see the article appear in Business Week or Information Week, or read the email announcing the first customer sale after launch.

Over the past ten years, I have discovered some tools and techniques that I believe are helpful in organizing, planning, and implementing product launches. They are presented here for you to consider and use. You may find them helpful, and you may also decide that some of them do not work in your organization or environment. I am constantly discovering new ways to do things, and you should be, too. The important thing is to use the techniques that do work.

I obtained my knowledge about launching products by getting my hands dirty, and by constant observation of real situations. My experience with product launch has been as a consultant and not as an employee. As such, I have been able to be more objective and less personally involved in the politics that go on during this stressful time. Some people believe that if you are not an employee, you have less at stake, that you don't "have skin in the game". Not so. As a consultant, my job and reputation is at stake. As an outsider, I need to remain unbiased. I get an opportunity to see it all. Often, people confided in me and asked my advice in situations where they would not have, had I been an employee. As a result, I got to experience the many points of view that people have in cross-functional launch teams, and this experience allowed me to put everything in the larger context of the company. This background has given me a unique opportunity to observe how the process works and doesn't work in many different companies. I hope that by sharing my knowledge with you, your experience with product launch will be made a little easier and that you find it a satisfying and worthwhile experience.

What's new in the second edition?

There are quite a few changes in this second edition of High Tech Product Launch. I've added many illustrations to the book to make it easier to understand the concepts. The examples from the first edition have been updated to the current timeframe. There is more content in the chapters on messaging, market analysis, competition and launch planning. I've added new content on business models and distribution, web intelligence, use of marketing messages, and launch budgeting.

Your comprehensive guide to product launch

This book covers all of the phases of product launch from gathering and analyzing data, through developing the market strategy and programs, and finally the implementation phase. You will learn the best ways to gather, analyze, and organize the data and information that is needed for launching your product. You will learn how to plan a product launch effectively, and how to implement the plan to meet your schedule objectives.

The three parts of the book cover the sequential phases of work that need to done from the beginning to the end. Part I, Data Gathering and Analysis, focuses on gathering the data and information that will be needed for planning the launch. The initial chapter is an overview of the entire launch process. The first step of the process is to define your product, and Chapter 2 describes an effective process for accomplishing that. The next important step is to define the company's overall strategic objectives for your product, and that is summarized in

Chapter 3.   Chapters 4 through 7 explain how to define the customer and assess the market, competition, and distribution channels.

Part II, Market Strategy and Programs, is all about how to analyze the information you have gathered, develop a marketing strategy, identify the marketing programs, and organize the information and analysis into a marketing plan. The analysis of the information and the definition of strategic objectives discussed in Part I help to formulate a positioning strategy, as described in Chapter 8.   From the positioning statements and other source material, the key messages are derived, and this is explained in Chapter 9. At this point, you can identify the right external marketing materials and programs that will communicate your messages to your customer, and that process is the focus of Chapter 10.   Chapter 11 describes how to develop effective public relations and advertising campaigns, and Chapter 12 is dedicated to the creation of internal marketing programs. All of the information, analysis, strategy, and programs are documented in the marketing plan, the subject of Chapter 13.

The third and last part of the book is the project management section. Chapter 14 describes the elements of the launch planning process, and Chapter 15 is focused on forming the launch team.   Chapter 16 is about allocating resources and creating launch schedules. Chapter 17 is all new, and guides you through development of the launch budget. Chapter 18 helps you compile all of the elements of the launch plan. Managing the challenging implementation phase is described in Chapter 19, which concludes part three of the book. Chapter 20 is focused on launch process improvement.

Throughout the book, the strategic thinking and the tactical implementation are woven together to present a complete guide to effective product launch. The chapters in the book can also be used as separate reference guides on their respective topics.

May all of your launches be wildly successful!

Catherine Kitcho
May 2005

PART I

Data Gathering
and Analysis

1

Product Launch as a Business Process

What is product launch?

The word *launch* means different things to different people. To some, it means the time when the product has completed the technical development phase and is ready to test. To others, it means the kickoff point for the beginning of a new product development cycle. And to still others, it refers to a high-profile advertising event that announces the product to the external world. Most often, however, *launch* refers to the process of preparing the market for your product and putting all the vehicles and infrastructure in place to get it to market. Launch is a business process that involves many different functional organizations in order to reach the key objective: getting the product to market. It means preparing the direct sales force and your channels for selling the product, introducing the product to the market through public relations activities, advertising, or other promotional programs, and announcing the product internally in the company to keep people informed and updated. For the purposes of this book, the definition of product launch includes all of those things. The launch phase of the new product cycle covers all of the external marketing and internal marketing activities that are undertaken to introduce the product to the target market.

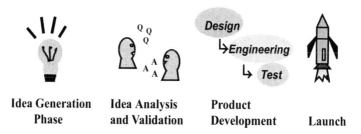

**Idea Generation   Idea Analysis   Product
Phase   and Validation   Development   Launch**

Figure 1.1 The New Product Cycle

Why high tech?

Product launch is different in every type of company, but high tech companies present a special challenge. All types of companies launch products and services to the market, but product launches in high tech companies tend to be among the most difficult and chaotic. What's so special about high tech companies? The life span of high tech products and the time to get them to market are usually shorter than in other types of companies. And if the company's strategy is to be first to market with the product, speed is even more critical. Many high tech companies haven't been in business very long and may still be in the growth or expansion stage. This means that they probably have few established business processes and procedures for managing product launches.

Sometimes these companies are launching into a crowded market or into one that has at least one major competitor. Large companies that may have many resources must still compete with fast, nimble little startups that might eat their lunch. Nimble little startups must compete with other startups, equally nimble. On top of that, the pace of technology development is usually faster in high tech companies than it is in consumer product companies. All this makes for an even more chaotic launch phase. If it's possible to create an effective launch process in a high tech environment, then it certainly is possible in a consumer products company. The principles in this book therefore apply to all sizes and types of companies, regardless of product or industry. The same principles also apply to companies that sell services rather than products.

The new product cycle

All new products go through a cycle, which has three major phases: the idea phase, the product development phase, and the launch phase. During the idea phase, there may be some investigation of customer needs and market trends, or perhaps a preliminary market study in order to validate the market demand for a product. Once the company is satisfied that there is market demand, the product development cycle begins, and during this cycle the product is prepared for the market. When the product has completed the development phase, the focus returns to the market, and the launch phase begins.

Idea Generation Phase	Idea Analysis and Validation	Product Development	Launch
-Formulate ideas -Choose ideas for further evaluation	-Market research -Identify customer need -Decide which ideas will be developed	-Design product -Build product -Customer feedback -Test	-Compile marketing plan -Develop and deploy all marketing programs

Figure 1.2 The Work of the New Product Cycle

During the launch phase, the market is prepared for the product. The launch phase itself consists of two different groups of activities: pre-launch activities, which include product/market assessment and marketing strategy development, and the actual launch activities, which include launch planning and implementation.

In the idea phase, the focus is on the market, in order to justify the development of the product. During the development phase, the focus is on technology and building the product. In the launch phase, the attention must again be on the market and preparing it for the product. Because the focus is not on the market right before the launch phase, and because the product development cycle takes so long, it is a challenge to quickly gear up for a very market-focused, short-lived launch phase. The first order of business is to update the information because market and customer factors will have changed by that time. Figure 1.3 shows what can happen:

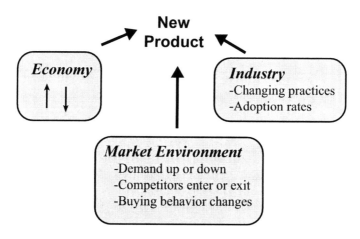

Figure 1.3 Updating Key Information
Before Launch

The economy may have experienced many fluctuations, and we have certainly witnessed this the last few years. These fluctuations affect overall spending levels of companies. Customers may not be as willing to buy during a downturn. The market environment can change considerably due to multiple factors. Demand for the product may go up or down, competitors leave or enter the market space, and your customers' buying behavior constantly changes no matter what. There are also industry factors; there may be changing practices due to regulations or innovation, and adoption rates of the technology may also change based on industry trends. Because of all this change, the first part of launch must include detailed data gathering and analysis so that you are familiar with the market environment into which you will be launching the product.

The corporate environment of product launch

Managing product launch in high tech companies has always been difficult. Most high tech companies of any size launch more than one product each year; larger firms might launch as many as 100 different products. The sequencing of product launches can be a significant management challenge in terms of prioritizing the launches and assigning adequate resources to the launch team. This challenge will become even more difficult as product development cycles continue to get shorter and shorter. In the last decade, the average development time for software products, for example, has decreased by one-half. At the same time, the useful life of products has also decreased. The Internet has created a whole new industry, and now requires new products to be compatible with this new way of doing business. As end users become accustomed to better, faster, cheaper products, they want even more functionality, speed, and economy in the next product that they buy. This means that product development organizations need to be in constant development and launch mode.

In order for a product launch to be successful, many problems and issues must be addressed and resolved. Some of the main areas of potential difficulty include staffing problems, planning problems, time pressures, and organizational issues.

Staffing

Putting together a product launch team is rarely a simple matter. Either no one wants to do it or everyone wants to do it. In many companies, the task of planning and managing product launch has no specific owner. These companies scramble to find someone to take on the assignment at the last minute, right before a product launch is scheduled to begin. Rarely is product launch staffed in advance. In other companies, there are *too many* people trying to execute a product launch, with no clear leader to take responsibility. When it comes to staffing product launches, it's either feast or famine.

Product launches rarely are staffed appropriately. Quite often, key resources are missing, usually on the marketing side. Because product launches are intermittent in most companies, when a product needs to be launched it is difficult to plan and allocate resources. The required personnel are usually assigned to other routine or strategic projects that make up their primary job duties. Product launches require the temporary assignment of key resources to multiple projects. This is especially critical in the marketing area, where key positions such as copy writer, multimedia designer, and launch manager may not be full-time positions. Sometimes, it is necessary to use temporary contractors or consultants to supplement the skills needed for the product launch team, and quite often, it is difficult to find qualified people on short notice.

Planning

In most cases, there are no plans in place for product launch. If there are plans, companies don't seem to follow them. Yet, planning on many different levels is essential for product launch. Without it you don't know where you're going, let alone how and when you're going to get there. Before you can even think about implementing a product launch, you must have a detailed marketing plan in place. The marketing plan integrates the strategic goals of the company with the positioning and messaging, leading to a detailed list of all marketing programs and deliverables needed for the launch.

In addition, you need a detailed launch plan to tell you how and when the launch will be implemented. The launch plan includes a detailed schedule for all deliverables that needs to be developed. It also includes a clear and concise description of roles and responsibilities of everyone associated with the launch. Budgets should be included. Without this level of planning, you don't know who the players are, where the handoffs occur, what the deadlines are, how information is communicated, and how much money you have to spend.

Most important of all, the entire launch team needs to have this information at the very beginning of the launch implementation, and they need to understand it. Rarely are all of these the process in order to have the final say.

The ideal world

As I said, I think we are getting better at implementing launches and now are starting to recognize launch as an important business process. But we still have work to do, and so I will repeat the ideal world versus real world comparison in this second edition of the book so that we can keep the ultimate goal in sight.

Ideally, here is how product launch works. The strategic objectives for the product are decided six months ahead of time and remain fixed until the product is launched. The market research has been continuing for eight months before launch, and the update will be completed four months before the launch date. The plan for all of the marketing programs and launch collateral is in place three months before launch; all resources who will support these deliverables have been identified, and everyone is ready to go. Three months before launch, the full launch plan is implemented, and everything happens on time, within budget and with a few days to spare. The team is efficient and effective, and everyone celebrates a successful launch.

The real world

In the real world, product launch rarely happens that way. More often, it unfolds like this. Someone in product management or marketing management discovers that they have a product announcement date approaching in less than three months. The launch team is not staffed, and there is no launch manager assigned. Someone finds a launch manager to start pulling together a team and a plan. Meanwhile, senior management starts to consider what the corporate messaging and strategic objectives need to be for the product, and some meetings are scheduled to start discussing these things. The launch manager finds out that the market research data is more than a year old and needs to be updated as soon as possible in order to identify the current competitors and determine which product features/functions need to be emphasized during the launch. The launch manager is unable to find sufficient resources in-house to create some of the marketing deliverables and scrambles to find outside vendors to do some of the collateral pieces, which affects the timeline for the internal corporate editing process. Meanwhile, senior management still has not decided what the key messages should be at the corporate level; all they've decided is that this product will be their first entry into a new vertical market. The launch manager re-commissions the market research group to take another look at this new market. Finally, the corporate messages are finalized so that the copy writing can begin for the collateral pieces. All this churning and rework results in a three-month slip in the launch date. Key messages don't develop in time, there is incomplete information available, the positioning is unfinished and the launch plan can't be finalized until all the resources are available. This scenario is very common and can happen over and over again in the same company.

What's the problem? (And the solution?)

Why don't things go ideally?   Most companies don't have or don't use an effective launch process. Because the launch phase is relatively short-lived, people do not consider it a key business process. It is ironic that the most critical business phase in the product development cycle is usually the least organized. The only way to organize the chaos of product launch is with an effective process. The fundamental elements of a business process include identification of the key individuals and organizations, the actions that must be taken, the products created by those actions, the interface points between the individuals, the timing and sequence of actions, and the decision points along the way.

By developing a solid launch team and a realistic launch plan, it is possible to launch a product in a very compressed period of time. The keys are effective communications and team management. In order for a launch to be successful, the launch team that's assembled must be made up of representatives from all of the cross-functional organizations that need to be involved, as well as outside vendors, as shown in Figure 1.4.

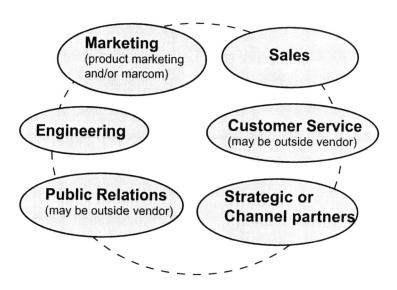

Figure 1.4 Cross-functional Involvement

These representatives need to be empowered to make decisions for their respective organizations. If the launch team can be assembled according to these guidelines, and if the launch manager uses sound project management principles to move the team forward on an agreed-upon path, then it is possible to complete a product launch in three months. This book shows you how to do that successfully, step by step.

The launch process is shown in Figure 1.5, and shows the work of launch corresponding to chapters 2 through 19 of this book.

Figure 1.5 The Launch Process

The remainder of the book will guide you through this launch process. You may choose to try out some of these steps in your own organization or adopt the entire sequence as your new launch process. Either approach will work. The important thing is to recognize that launch is indeed an important and critical business process, and if followed with diligence, will help you get your new product to market on time.

Using the process if you are a small company or startup

Much of this book is focused on product launch in medium to large sized companies that may have many departments and organizations that support product launch. If you are in a startup or small company, the principles are the same, but there is a difference of scale. Instead of having many individuals representing different organizations on your launch team, you may only have one or two who wear a lot of different hats. That's fine, and the process will still work. The important thing is to gather all of the information that you need, and examine all the perspectives that those functions represent.

If you sell services

Launching service offerings is similar to launching products, except what you sell to your customers is not as tangible as selling a product. Again, the principles are still the same. When you do product definition and competitive analysis, you may have a little less detail and fewer bases for comparison than you would for a product. In competitive analysis, you will likely put more focus on the company level than at the "product" level. Many high tech companies are developing service offerings in addition to products that they may already sell. Many products such as software can now be sold in the form of a subscription service. Also, services can supplement revenue from products. If you sell services as a product and services mix, you may be launching the services at the same time as the product. That may mean developing an additional set of messages and also some different marketing materials that explain what you offer and how the services are packaged.

If you sell to consumers and not businesses

Many high technology products are sold to the consumer market rather than in the business-to-business market. The only differences between the two markets are buying decisions and segmentation. For consumer markets, there are fewer individuals to influence before purchase; with business markets, there may be layers of individuals that need be influenced to effect a buying decision. Segmentation also may be a little trickier with consumer markets because the market size is greater. Again, the basic principles are the same and the process will work.

2

Product Definition

The starting point of an effective product launch process is to define the product. This may seem like an unnecessary step to some people; after all, if you are doing a product launch, don't you already know what the product is? Not necessarily. The act of writing out a detailed description of the product forces the thinking required to answer two key questions:

-Is this product a new, discrete offering?
-Is the product ready to be launched?

These two questions need to be answered in the affirmative if you are going to execute a full-blown product launch. If the answer to either question is no, then you probably don't need a launch, or at least not yet.

What is "new"?

How do you determine if a product is a new and discrete offering? A product might be new to the company, new to the industry, new to the customer base, or may employ new technologies. If this product offers new functionality that existing products don't have, then it should be regarded as a new product. Sometimes an existing product is reconfigured or repackaged for a new target customer or market segment, where the product will be used to solve a different customer need. That should also be treated as a new product. When you are preparing to develop or launch a new product, who determines that the product is *new*? It might be the CEO, the technical team, the business development director, or the marketing team who actually gives the product the *new* designation on the basis of some set of criteria. The *new* designation might mean something entirely different to employees inside the company than it does to the external market. The new product might require varying degrees of effort to launch, from merely updating a datasheet to hiring a new sales force in order to enter a new market niche.

New Product, Existing Customers

Selling a new product to existing customers may be just a matter of creating additional sales collateral for the new product and training the sales force on how to sell it and compare it to existing products. It's important to point out the benefits of the new product, but also important to tread lightly. Your customers might be very happy with their X2005 Server Accelerator that had a learning curve of 2.6 years and are just not ready to start that process again. Still other customers always want the newest, latest solution available. It's important to offer choice, but to respect that choice. In order to be effective, sales people must have a firm grasp on exactly what's new about the new product.

New Product, New Customers

Selling to new customers is always more complex, even if you're just selling your existing products. But selling new products to a new group of customers is akin to starting a whole new company. Not only do you have to establish a new presence in the market, but you also must implement many marketing programs to develop awareness of the product and convince customers to buy it. This approach may require the involvement of a cross-functional team to develop a plan for entering the market, including business development people, marketing strategists to decide when and where to roll out marketing programs, and sales managers to plan sales staffing and training.

Determining whether the product is new is very important, because if the product is not new, positioning and promoting the product will be very difficult and confusing for customers. In that situation, the target customer might perceive the "new" designation as merely a marketing ploy; it's not really a new product to them. Perception is the key, especially when it comes to customers. However, if an otherwise new product is part of a larger solution and cannot function as a standalone product, then it probably would not be a discrete offering. This is important because product launches are expensive efforts, and there must be some return on investment. In the case where the product cannot stand on its own, it may pay to wait until the complete solution is ready to launch, rather than just launching one part of it.

Is the product ready to be launched?

Readiness for launch is another key issue because you don't want to waste the time and money unless the product is ready for the market. The main question here is: when will the product be available? This point in time is sometimes referred to as the general availability date or "GA" date. If this date is more than three months into the future, then it may be too early to start the launch process. It is possible that the product is not even complete yet, or worse, that the product may not even work. Has the product been tested internally? Have beta tests with customers started, or will they start in the near future?

Internal testing of the product should be completed before launch begins, and beta tests should either be underway or scheduled such that the testing phase will be complete before product announcement date. It is very risky to begin a product launch and then be embarrassed because the product does not function as intended; this wastes money and damages your company's credibility in the marketplace.

Some companies don't begin the product launch until the pricing for the product has been established. One of the reasons that companies wait for pricing information is so that the marketing and launch resources can be allocated appropriately. A product that sells for a low price may have a lower priority in the company than one that is priced at a higher level. Another reason to have the pricing information at the beginning of the launch process is that it helps the competitive analysis and subsequently, the positioning of the product. These two marketing activities need to be done early in the launch process; having the pricing data at the beginning saves time.

The product description

If you have determined that there is a launchable product, then the product needs to be clearly defined in a document. This document may take many forms and have slightly different names, such as product spec, product design plan, or product note. Whatever you decide to call it, this product description document will serve as a valuable guide during the product launch process. It does not have to be a very long document; the content is more important than the volume of information. At a minimum, the document should include the functions, features and technical specifications of the product, how it was designed and developed, a description of the product's relationship with other products in the company, compatibility with industry standards and other companion products, and how the product will be supported during and after the sales cycle. These topics are addressed in the remainder of this chapter.

Product functionality

There are several steps involved in defining the product. Assuming that there is a product that is new and ready to launch as previously determined, you need to define what the product is. Start with general terms and categories, such as hardware, software, system, microchip, equipment, services, etc., and write down the terms that apply to your product. With high tech products, you will soon find yourself at the next step: defining what the product does, or its functionality. Write down all of the action verbs that indicate how the product functions.

Using the example of a security firewall, the category could be either hardware or software; we'll assume software for this example. Some of the functions are:

     -Monitors network and PC connections to the Internet
     -Identifies and categorizes threats
     -Sends message about threat to user
     -Blocks or permits traffic as per user instructions
     -Compiles historical record of threats for reporting

Once this initial list is complete, then you need to add to it. Highlight or underline what is new. Then highlight what you feel is unique; i.e. what none of the competing products can do. The last step is to write down what the product cannot do, because you will need that information later when you compare your product to that of your competitors' products. This highlighted list now forms a basis for determining some of the messages that need to be developed during the launch process.

Messages need to emphasize what is new about the product and identify the differentiating features from those of your competitors' products. In summary, you need to define what the product is, what the product does, highlight what is new, and define what the product doesn't do.

Product features

Key technical features need to be defined next. Product features are partly quantitative and partly qualitative. The quantitative portion usually refers to performance, capacity, size or complexity. The qualitative description may include references to other products such as compatible platforms, operating systems and industry standards. Technical features are mostly easily presented in a bulleted list, for example:

        -Can be deployed on single PC or network
        -Requires 512 MB RAM
        -Supports broadband or dial-up connections
        -Compatible with Windows NT, 2000, XP

Information about features is very important for the launch process, because it helps with competitive positioning, and later on in the launch process, it helps in the development of certain types of collateral, such as datasheets and white papers.

Development history and product roadmap

It is quite helpful for the launch team to understand the history of the development process for the product. If possible, try to find out how the product idea was first generated. If the idea came from a customer, this creates a great marketing story that can be leveraged during the launch. If the original idea came from company-internal sources, then a slightly different message would need to be crafted; the emphasis would instead be on the "continuous product innovation record" of the company.

Sometimes, products have been in the development process for a long time, due to technical challenges, complexity, or degree of innovation required for the product. Overcoming these challenges to finally launch the product is certainly a relief for the company, but more importantly, this can be leveraged in marketing messages for the launch.

Understanding where the new product fits in a company's product line or product family is also very important in determining the overall launch strategy. Where in the product roadmap is this product? If this is not the first product to be launched in a series, were there successful (or unsuccessful) launches for the products that preceded this product? What product functionality does this new product have that the others did not have? Does the new product provide improved performance (faster, more accurate, more reliable)? Does the new product offer better compatibility with other products that are used in its most common applications? Is the new product the beginning of a new line of products that the company will be developing going forward? What will be the price points for the new product? And most importantly, will the new product reduce interest in the company's existing products or make them obsolete? The answers to these questions will help define what functionality or messages need to be emphasized or de-emphasized during the new launch. If this is the first product in a new family, and others are to follow over the next year, it may be advisable to find out the strategy for the whole product line first, so that the first entry into the market can set the stage for future product announcements.

Development specifications

Detailed specifications should also be included in the product description document. These will be helpful during the beta testing phase, when product performance will be tested by one or more customers, and performance can be measured against the intended specifications. This information may also be necessary for developing the training materials that will be needed during and after the launch process. This is especially true if the product requires any degree of customization or requires installation at the customer's location. In that case, the specifications may be needed in order to determine that the product is functioning properly.

Industry standards

For some products, compatibility with evolving or established industry standards is critical to success. If your new product is indeed compatible with the right standards, then this should be clearly spelled out in the product description. Highlighting this compatibility in marketing deliverables may be important for customer buying decisions related to technical compatibility or product quality.

Partners' products

Sometimes, products are designed to be used with other technology products for basic functionality or enhanced performance. These other products might be those of a strategic partner or another company's product that is becoming a widely-accepted standard. In either case, including this information in the marketing materials for your product enhances the acceptance of your product in the market. In a sense, you can "piggyback" on to the brand recognition that these other companies have in the general marketplace. This information needs to be included in the product description.

Beta test program

The plan for beta testing should be defined in the product description. At a minimum, the beta testing plan should identify beta customer candidates by name, a description of the selection process, the testing objectives for each candidate, and the schedule for the beta testing phase. Often, beta testing programs involve a contractual arrangement, whereby the customer is allowed to keep the product for free or for minimal cost in exchange for acting as an account reference. The terms and conditions of the beta test program should also be described in the product description document. This is important to the launch because it is highly desirable to have one or more solid customer stories and customer quotes to use during the public relations campaign, as well as in some of the marketing collateral. If these arrangements are made well in advance, the customers can provide feedback when it is needed during launch.

Product documentation

The phrase "the product isn't done until the paperwork's done" is often ignored with high tech products, in the rush to get the product to market. Additionally, few people enjoy the process of creating product documentation such as user manuals. Consequently, the product documentation is usually the last thing on the list to do before the product completes the development cycle. However, it is important for the launch team to communicate with the documentation group so that there is consistency in product naming and terms that are used to describe functionality. There should not be one set of terminology used in the documentation and another, different set used in the collateral such as datasheets or training materials created during launch. In the product description document, the list of product documentation and schedule for development should be identified so that the efforts can be coordinated.

Sales support

High tech products often require installation or some degree of customization. If that is the case, then the product description document needs to identify these requirements. In addition, any installation guides should be listed, along with any other resources available to the sales team to help sell the product. These may include configuration guides, product selection charts, pricing guides, and lists of product options. These materials may need to be packaged into some sort of sales kit during the product launch, and knowing this early in the launch will help the launch team plan for this deliverable.

If customization is going to be needed, then the group who will provide the services should be identified in the product description document. Contact names and numbers and the process for engaging any services groups should also be described. Internal or external services groups that support customization will need some internal marketing information when the product is launched so they can be prepared to service the customers. The launch team will need to know this ahead of time in order to make the required information available during the launch.

Post-sales support

It is critical to new product success that a plan is put in place for the "whole product", which refers to all of the services needed to deliver the full value of the product to the customer. The whole product usually includes the product, support to install the product, training, and a communications path for receiving technical or business support after the sale. During product launch, all of the associated services should be launched along with the product. That's why they need to be identified in the product description document. Which organization will install the product? Who will train the customer if required? Who does the customer call to receive support after the sale? What processes are in place to deliver the services to the customer, and which groups have the charter to do this? All of these questions need to be answered in the product description document.

Product training

Depending upon the complexity of the product, some degree of training may be needed for the sales force, channel partners, or customers. The product description document should identify how much training is required, when it needs to be delivered, and which groups need to be trained. Sometimes, a tremendous amount of training material needs to be developed during the launch process. Knowing this ahead of time will help the launch team allocate the resources and find the source content experts who can help provide the technical information that needs to be conveyed during the training process.

Taking the time to fully characterize and define the product will prove to be time well spent as the launch phase progresses. The product definition will provide a baseline during the marketing strategy phase, so that your product can be positioned properly in the target market for maximum impact.

3

Strategic Objectives

The business objectives of the company set the overall direction for a product launch. You need to have a clear understanding of the strategy of the company before planning a product launch to ensure that the launch process will achieve the desired business results. In effect, the strategic objectives of the company form the basis of your product launch strategy. When established at the beginning of the process, the launch strategy will drive the how and the when for the product launch. The launch strategy will define the emphasis that needs to be placed on various external and internal marketing programs and will determine the overall positioning of the product in the marketplace. This is part of the how. The when is the product launch date, a key factor in planning the entire launch process. The launch date will determine the overall launch plan and schedule.

Strategic objectives are established by the senior management of the company and are updated on a regular basis to reflect current economic and market conditions. Many companies redefine strategic objectives at the beginning of a new fiscal year; some companies update them more frequently in response to business operating performance. Sometimes these strategic objectives are communicated to all employees via email, the company intranet, presentations, or all-hands meetings. These objectives are usually the "official" strategic objectives, chosen for their motivational impact and consistency with corporate mission statements. Quite often, there are additional business objectives that are more closely held within senior management, and those are the ones that may greatly impact product launches. It is important to communicate with senior management at the beginning of the launch process to obtain an update on the current strategic thinking of the company. Usually, the CFO and/or Vice-President of Marketing are the best candidates to supply this information. The best way to accomplish this task is to schedule a meeting with these individuals and interview them about their current strategic thinking for your launch. If they are willing and have the time, it's also a good idea to have them give a presentation to the launch team about strategy.

What are strategic objectives?

The senior management of the company set the business goals and future direction as part of long-term strategic planning. Strategic objectives are usually articulated in terms of measurable goals that can realistically be attained within a year or a quarter. These goals may be related to growth, strategic partnering, market position, or diversification. Here are some examples:

> *Our mission is to successfully enter the small business market with a new product within the next year.*

> *Through acquisition, we will increase our capabilities in database services.*

> *Our goal is to increase revenues by 10% by the second quarter of this year.*

It is important to understand these objectives because management may be viewing your product as the key to attaining the strategic goals. Knowing this will help the launch team understand the priority of the launch in the big picture and will help guide the team in allocating launch resources and determining which marketing programs will be most effective for the launch. A few examples will illustrate how this works.

Growth

Company growth is usually regarded as a respectable goal. Shareholders and employees want to be associated with a company that offers some return on investment and some job security. Determining the rate of growth, however, is difficult. A number of factors are involved, including external forces such as market conditions, competition, and state of the economy. Internal factors include the company's ability to recruit new staff, efficiency of the R&D group, and financial status of the company. Senior management will consider all of the necessary external and internal factors when determining the growth rate goal, which is usually expressed as a percentage increase in revenue, profit, headcount, or market share.

If growth is a strategic objective, the rate of new product development and launches may increase substantially. In the rush to get more products to market, companies can fall into the pattern of getting the products out the door without regard for positioning or putting the right marketing vehicles into place for reaching the market.

In one actual case, a company that was launching an average of one product per year suddenly was faced with launching ten products per year in order to meet their growth goal. Unfortunately, there were inadequate marketing resources in place to launch that many products, and the company had to bring in contractors and consultants in order to keep up. There was no one to develop an overall strategy for all of the products, creating a lack of consistency in the external marketing programs that were eventually implemented. The press and analysts' tour for the first two products went well, but by the time the third product was launched, the trade press began to question what was newsworthy about these products. It is difficult to engage the attention of the same analysts and trade press editors ten times in one year, unless you have some overall, incremental strategy that creates a compelling story about your company. In this case, if the company had taken the time to articulate the product strategy that corresponded with their growth goal and communicated that strategy during the press tour, their launches might have had more impact.

Sometimes growth happens too quickly in a company, and the launch processes don't have a chance to evolve to meet the pace of change. Sometimes growth itself is a competitive advantage, and getting the products to market quickly becomes more important than careful positioning. In another case, a company grew so quickly over a period of two years, that they didn't have time to develop or use an effective launch process. Their strategic goal was to maintain their position as leader in their market through growth in new products. As they kept reorganizing, first by product line and then again by market segment, they became more decentralized. Product launches were done differently in each decentralized group, according to their own changing whims and budgets. This led to much inconsistency and confusion in the marketplace because the sales collateral, training materials, and even the company website contained such a variety of messages about the products and the company. If the environment in your company is similar, it may be a good idea to contact the top marketing executive in the company to obtain clear guidance on which launch process to follow, your product's relative rank of importance to the company, and success criteria for the launch.

Changing corporate image

Sometimes companies find it necessary to change their corporate image because they are undergoing some type of transition, such as entering new markets, creating new core businesses, or closing out maturing product lines. Re-branding may be required, sometimes involving a change in logo or tag lines, or the development of a new advertising campaign. If an image change is happening in your company, you need to be aware of the new corporate-level messages about the company that will be part of the new image. Some examples include changing from a software company to a services company, becoming more innovative, expanding globally, setting a new industry standard, focusing on customer satisfaction, or offering end-to-end systems and services. These new messages will need to flow down to the product-level messages that will be contained in all of the marketing deliverables for the launch. The key words of the new image (such as those highlighted in the examples above) should be used in the marketing materials you develop for the launch. Your product will help to establish the new image in the marketplace, effectively repositioning the company.

Change in core business

As companies grow and change, it often becomes necessary to add new, complementary businesses. This is especially true in high tech companies because of the pace of technology evolution. For example, during most of the last five to ten years, the majority of the advancements in the field of computing have been in software and not hardware. Companies that used to be the icons of hardware innovation suddenly found themselves in the software business in order to remain a market player. The Internet has triggered another wave of change in high tech companies. Any new trend in technology creates new opportunity, and along with it, the pressure to compete and respond to changing demand and evolving standards.

If adding core businesses is one of your company's strategic objectives, it may mean that the new product that you're launching will be sold to existing customers, or that the new product will be sold to new customers. This will impact the launch in terms of positioning and choice of marketing programs. If the product is being sold to existing customers in the current market segment, then the benefits of the new product need to be emphasized in order to educate the customers. If the new product will be sold to new customers, then new market research will likely have to be conducted in order to identify the characteristics of the new customer and market. It is also likely that with a new market, a market entry strategy will need to be implemented in order to develop awareness for the company before the product is launched. This may require additional, different types of marketing programs first to create the awareness and then to follow up with more detailed information about the product.

Acquisitions

Sometimes it is more expedient and cost effective for companies to acquire other companies than to develop new products or to enter new markets on their own. It's the classic "make versus buy" decision. Companies that are cash-rich or that are in a steady growth mode often do this to compete more effectively.

If acquisitions are part of your company's strategy, then you need to address how the acquired company's products compare to the one that you will be launching. Sometimes, there is an overlap of functionality that occurs between products from both companies. In one example, a company acquired another company right in the middle of the launch of a key product. The acquired company and technology strengthened the new product in terms of end-to-end functionality, so the launch date was moved out in time in order to accommodate the new functionality. By delaying, the company was able to create a much stronger message going into a new market.

If there is no overlap with the acquired company's products, there may still be some corporate messages that need to flow down into the product-level messages for your launch. For example, suppose a wireless adapter company acquires a company that develops messaging software, and you are launching the new adapter hardware. You could talk about the complete range of mobile communications that are possible when using your hardware adapter, such as Internet access, email, instant messaging, images, audio or video. You might even refer to the acquired company's messaging software. Sometimes, bundling the combined products together in a marketing campaign creates opportunities to reach a larger market and serves the business objective of the acquisition.

Downsizing

Downsizing is often thought of as the opposite of growth, but that isn't necessarily the case. Reducing business operations through reduction in staff or by selling off selective business units is a common strategic objective. It doesn't always mean that the company is going out of business. Downsizing may mean that there is renewed emphasis and focus on the products that will remain in the company. This is important to know when planning a product launch, because it may be necessary to address any concerns from analysts and trade press about the stability of the company. This reassurance would be developed as part of the messages in all of the external marketing materials.

Competitive strategy

Strategic objectives sometimes call for action against a specific competitor, in order to increase market share or to move up in the relative ranking in the market. Examples might be statements such as:

Surpass Intel in processor performance.

Beat Dell to market with ultra-light low-priced laptops.

These types of strategic objectives are designed to motivate all employees to improve company performance. For the product launch team, this situation will require more careful attention to competitive analysis, especially for the identified competitor. It may also be necessary to use message statements that directly compare your company's products with the specified competitor during the marketing and public relations campaign.

Diversification

This is similar to a change in core business, but diversification is usually a larger effort across the company to innovate and to develop new businesses. Sometimes companies will develop formal diversification programs. For example, companies will sometimes incentivize their sales force to find new business opportunities while serving existing customers, or will direct the business development group to seek out new opportunities. Once the areas of diversification are identified, the launch team will need to build in positioning to take this into account. Sometimes messages will reflect a company's diversification strategy: "We now provide managed services to help you get the most out of our data warehouse systems." During a launch, you are preparing the market for the product, and that sometimes involves updating and educating the market about what is new in the company, especially if the product you're launching is an integral piece of the new strategic direction.

Going public

Sometimes product launches are tied to the company's plan for an initial public offering (IPO). If an IPO will follow a product launch, then management may be waiting for market response to the launched product before they determine the exact timing of the offering. If that is the case, then more focus needs to be placed on the press and analyst programs during the launch in order to create more awareness and ultimately, investor interest in the stock offering.

If an IPO precedes a product launch, then it is advisable to identify what analysts said about the company and its stock offering in terms of strategic direction for the company and the products. There may have been promises made about your product at the time that will need to be addressed in the marketing materials during the launch. You will need to explain how the product is fulfilling the earlier promises that were made.

Strategic partnering

Existing partnerships and alliances create many marketing opportunities for a company, and sometimes these business relationships are involved in specific strategic objectives.

For example, consider the situation of a joint development partnership between your company and another company, when finally, the time has come to launch the new product that was developed by the combined team. In this situation, the launch efforts of both companies essentially need to be married together, which can be a coordination nightmare for both launch teams. Joint product announcements and launches can create conflicts in decision-making, positioning, and messaging. It is best to meet with the strategic partner's launch team as early as possible so that a mutually acceptable set of roles and responsibilities can be developed. Combined product launches of strategic partners can have a powerful impact on the market, but they require the cooperation and commitment of both business entities to be successful.

Formulating the launch strategy

The foregoing examples illustrate the many ways that strategic directions can impact your launch strategy. Once you have identified the strategic objectives, then it is advisable to develop some high-level corporate messages that will help achieve the business results. Chapter 9 is focused on how to develop these messages. You will need them later on when the marketing plan is developed. The other key task at this point is to identify the areas of emphasis for the launch. Is more focus needed on the public relations campaign than on sales collateral? Do we need to pay closer attention to the competition? Prioritizing will help to allocate the resources and budget for the launch effectively.

Setting the launch date

Many strategic business factors have an impact on the choice of launch date. General availability of the product is usually a very significant factor, if not the most important. Announcing the product to the outside world without the product being available can create more damage to company credibility than if the product was not announced at all. Doing so may give your competitors some ammunition to use regarding your company's ability to deliver.

The season of the year can also be a factor in launch date selection, especially if a press tour or campaign is part of the launch. Analysts and press may not be accessible during certain times of the year, such as summer (mid-June to mid-August). Another time of the year in which it is inadvisable to launch products is the last two months of the year - November and December - due to the holidays.

Timing of one product launch relative to launches of other products being released is another important consideration. If two launches occur too close together in time, one could overshadow the other in the marketplace. And if the products can't logically be combined into one announcement or launch, then there must be sufficient time in between.

Maintaining momentum in the market, a "drumbeat" approach, is another possible strategy that can affect launch dates. Sometimes, a steady stream of launches or announcements at specific intervals is the best plan, particularly for a company that launches several products each year.

Other marketing events such as trade shows, or corporate events such as annual meetings or user group conferences, can also help determine the time of greatest impact for product launch. A trade show may be a good venue for a major product announcement, because the trade press is usually present at these shows, and you have a captive audience. On the other hand, if everyone is waiting for a major trade show to announce their product, yours may be lost in the noise. Competitive intelligence helps in making this decision; you may know ahead of time whether any of your competitors will also be announcing at the same time. This allows you to decide whether or not to announce at a trade show.

A corporate event where customers are present may also be an excellent venue for announcing a product. Having a critical mass of customers in one place is a golden opportunity to use the event itself as a marketing program and to receive immediate feedback on your new product. Slide presentations or handouts for the event can contain marketing information on the product being launched, saving mailing or distribution costs.

Sometimes senior management may dictate the announcement date for the product. However your company arrives at the announcement date, establish the date as early as possible after receiving management approval so that the launch plan can be developed.

A core set of strategic objectives developed early in the launch process will help set the direction for the launch. Someone once said that you need to know where you are going before you can figure out how to get there. Defining strategic objectives is the first step in figuring out where you are going. The next steps are defining your customer and characterizing your target market.

4

The Customer

Now that you have analyzed your product in detail, and you know how the product fits into the strategic plan for your company, it is time to take an in-depth look at your target customer. The objective is to more fully understand who your customer is and his or her buying behavior. This understanding will enable you to position your product effectively in the market in order to reach those customers and to develop messages for your marketing materials that will get your customer's attention.

Companies spend millions of dollars each year trying to understand the buying behavior of customers. While these companies are studying their target customer, some other company is trying to understand their own customers' buying behavior. Wouldn't it be easier if we all could just go to a big conference somewhere, tell each other how we buy products and services, and get it over with? It's tempting to think of such a scene, but the reality is that customers and you and I change our buying habits over time. As we buy products and services, and as technology evolves, we look for different features and functionality and different levels of customer support. We learn from our mistakes and keep searching for the perfect product. And so, the game begins again. Studying customer behavior is a continuous cycle.

Tapping into your existing customer base

Most companies have a pretty good understanding of their customers, or so they claim. However, customers change their buying habits, mood, and perceptions, and OFTEN. After all, customers are (unfortunately) humans. They change their attitudes, their habits, and their opinion of your products. This happens without warning or provocation and for reasons only known to them. If you don't pay attention to what your customers are doing, your whole business can unravel. It is crucial to continuously review and update your understanding of your target customer.

If you're in the business-to-business marketplace, you should constantly be monitoring the business news and your customers' websites to understanding what's happening in their companies. If your customer had a bad quarter, what will that do to your plans to sell them the product you are launching? There may also be good news. Maybe you read that your customer contact person has just been promoted; that should give you a golden opportunity to send a congratulatory message and get an update on what the person's new job will be. It could mean more opportunities to sell them the new product or gather critical feedback.

You may have just one market segment, but within that segment the customers' behavior may vary all over the map. Customers may have differing decision authority for purchases. Constant and ongoing feedback measurement is necessary to understand your customer's behavior over a period of time. Engage your sales force in this effort to assess changes in customer behavior. During an initial sale, customer behavior may be entirely different from that of a subsequent sale. It's important for a salesperson to do a quick and informal survey after every sale. It can be done in the form of a few email questions or a phone call. Respect your customer's time. Give them an opportunity to make suggestions to improve their customer experience further. If there are long time intervals between sales or customer contacts, initiate a call or email to find out what's new with your customer and how they are doing with your product or service.

When you have the opportunity to gather information from your customers directly, focus on listening instead of doing all the talking. Humans communicate more than just words. You can gather information from the person's tone, attitude, and willingness to talk. Sometimes there is information in what is NOT said.

Who is your customer?

The best place to start is to define your target customer. For instance, for products that are sold to other businesses (as distinct from products sold to individual consumers), you might ask the following questions about the individuals in those companies that you need to reach with your product. Who are they? Where are they in the organization; are they managers, part of a team, an executive? What department are they in - business units, engineering, development, marketing or sales? Once you have an idea where they are in the organization, define what those customers do in a given day. What business processes do they use? What technology? What makes their job difficult, and what would make their job easier? What would save them time or money or advance their careers? Do they manage a budget or even have a budget? What kinds of decisions can they make at their level in the organization? Mentally follow a typical customer around for a day to get a better sense of what his or her issues and business problems might be - those are the ones that you might be able to solve with your product or service.

In order to answer these questions, you may need to talk with existing customers or potential new customers in person. If you have the time and budget to do this, it is a worthwhile exercise, especially because of constantly changing customer buying behavior. The more you know about your customer, the more current information you will have to position and launch your new product. Figure 4.1 is a checklist of questions to ask a potential customer.

What to Ask a Potential Customer

-*What's your most pressing business issue?*
-*How are you addressing this now?*
-*What obstacles are there to solving the problem?*
-*When does the problem need to be solved?*
-*Who decides how the problem will be solved?*
-*Do you have the budget to solve the problem?*
-*Who writes the check?*

Figure 4.1 Customer Questions

Customer buying behavior

The best way to begin to understand your customer is to identify a real or fictitious individual to study. If you will be selling your product to another business, then it is important to identify your customer's relative position in the organization, his or her job title, purchasing authority, and business responsibilities. In business-to-business marketing, your customer is usually the decision maker who buys your product or service. However, you shouldn't assume that all of your marketing material is targeted only for that individual. There are other "influencers" in the organization as well. These are individuals who manage the decision makers, or those who control a budget, or those that have signature authority to sign the check.

If you will be selling your product directly to consumers, then you will need to find some demographic data about them, including where they are located; age, gender and income level; and buying habits such as the frequency of purchasing certain items. By studying this information, it is possible to begin to characterize buying behavior.

Let's take an example of a business-to-business customer, an IT director within a large company. The product that you want to sell to this customer is a network testing tool. After going through your contact list, you discover that one of your former coworkers is now an IT director in a high tech company, and you decide to take him to lunch to find out more about what he does. After this discussion, you learn that his primary job responsibilities include overseeing the purchase of all network hardware and software, managing network availability, and troubleshooting system-wide problems. He manages six network engineers. As the IT director, he manages the overall IT budget. Sometimes, if he is able to test a new software tool and likes it, he will buy it if it will help improve their service response time. He likes to test out new software tools during alpha and beta testing, before they are ready for the market.

From this short lunch meeting, here is what you have learned about your target customer:

-Title: IT Director
-Relative organizational position: senior IT manager
-Business problem: maintain network availability
-Purchasing authority: has purchasing authority
-Other: candidate for beta test

You now have some information about the buying behavior of your target customer. You know that the IT director has purchasing authority, and that maintaining network availability is a key area of a director's responsibility. You also believe that beta testing might be a good way to develop awareness of the product with your target customer, and also to obtain feedback about the product to help your marketing campaign.

Now let's use an example of business to consumer marketing. In this situation, assume that the product is an Internet phone (that employs voice-over-IP technology). You have purchased market research studies on landline phone rates and Internet usage in ten major metropolitan areas. The numbers look very good in terms of the rate comparison. The task is to determine how many customers would be interested in using an Internet phone instead of a conventional landline. Let's assume that you contract with a market research firm to do a focus group in selected cities, and you observe the reactions of some of the consumers during these sessions. These focus group participants are chosen on the basis of Internet usage. During the focus group session, several consumers react favorably to the look of the phone and the proposed service rates. However, many participants are worried about not having phone service during a power outage; if their computer is down, they have no way to make calls. Another individual cannot grasp why a person couldn't just use a cell phone instead, and with the number of affordable rate plans available today, the cost isn't really that much more.

At first glance, these observations might seem very discouraging. However, let's summarize what was learned about consumer buying behavior during this focus group scenario:

- Price and value are important considerations for consumers
- Consumers like the technology concept, and the look of the product is appealing
- The proposed service rates are acceptable
- Consumers want a reliable way to communicate during emergencies
- Some consumers are satisfied with alternatives already available to them (cell phones)

In selling this product to consumers, you would need to position the product as an alternative means of telecommunication, but not necessarily a primary means of telecommunication. The favorable service rates would have to be emphasized so that the consumer thinks the price is acceptable for an alternative or "optional" service. One of the key messages would have to be the convenience of being able to make and receive calls while using the Internet. The marketing literature should have photos of the product that highlight its technology appeal. The safety issues could be addressed by adding a "Questions and Answers" section in the marketing literature. These are some of the ways to inform the consumers about your product and begin to resolve their buying issues.

Customer problem

The most important information about your customers is the problem they have that your product can solve for them. Hopefully, your product started out as an idea that was based on a customer need or problem. In high tech companies, this isn't always the case. It's more common to develop a product and then look for a customer ("product push"). Companies are getting better at creating and developing products in response to the customer's need, the so-called "market pull" approach. Figure 4.2 illustrates the difference between market pull and product push.

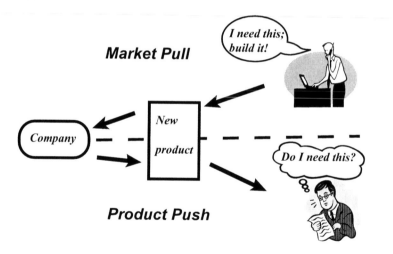

Figure 4.2 Market Pull versus Product Push

Now that your product has been developed and is ready to launch, you need to validate that the customer still has the problem. It is necessary to do this because quite a bit of time may have passed during the development phase of the product.

The customer problem should be defined in a descriptive statement. Using an example of a testing tool for IT Directors, the customer problem might be:

> *IT Directors need to increase network uptime.*

Quite often, the customer need or problem is expressed in objective or quantitative terms, such as "reducing time or costs by x percent", "increasing efficiency or output volume by x amount". In these instances, the need relates to time or money. An example:

> *Based on our last customer survey, the manager of customer support needs to reduce caller wait time by 50%.*

Sometimes, the customer problem is more subjective or qualitative. Examples are "increased customer satisfaction", "added value", "mutual benefit", "improving business relationships", "providing new opportunities", "enabling change", and "improving quality". An example of a qualitative statement is:

> *The participants in our last user's conference concluded that the technical demos of the product allowed them to understand how to use the product in new ways.*

These qualitative factors are a matter of perception, involving personal points of view. Qualitative needs or problems are more difficult to characterize and measure. It is more difficult to demonstrate that a product meets a qualitative need, because that is a matter of opinion. This could present a challenge in terms of how the messages in the marketing literature are crafted.

In most cases, the customer problem has both a quantitative and qualitative component, or several of each type. Because of this, you may have some choices as to which components to emphasize in your marketing campaign.

As a product moves from the idea stage through the development phase, additional customer benefits may be discovered that were not intentionally designed into the product. Sometimes these customer benefits may even be identified during the beta testing phase, which is very late in the process. For example, in one company, a product was designed that was supposed to centralize network-wide control at a desktop (its primary functionality). This was supposed to create increased productivity for the network administrators. When the product was tested by the beta customers, they discovered that the product allowed them to rapidly reroute high-volume network traffic, increasing the rate of response for their sales staff, which ultimately increased sales. During the launch, the rerouting benefit was emphasized in the marketing materials because it related to an economic benefit to the customer. This created a more powerful message for the product. This example underscores the importance of revisiting the customer needs and benefits during the launch phase; doing so may yield significant data for positioning the product in the best possible light.

The customer value proposition

Once you have identified and characterized the customer's problem, you need to find out how the product will be used and who will use it. What value does it provide to each person who will use the product? It is critical to determine what the product solution may be worth to your customers in terms of economic benefit and what they are willing to pay for achieving the economic benefit. This is known as the customer's value proposition. Customers view this as a return on their investment in the product. That also influences how much they are willing to pay for it. During the idea phase or the early stages of product development, the pricing needs to be determined for the product. The customer's opinion of value and price should be the most important determinant of price. Product pricing needs to be complete at the time of product launch because it affects marketing messages as well as internal marketing materials such as sales training guides and price lists.

Who uses the product is also critical, because you may need to create marketing programs that will reach all levels of end users of the product. Users may be in different departments or organizations. The beta testing phase is also a time to observe all of the possible users of the product.

Studying customers

There are many ways to obtain information about customers. Most of the information about customers comes from either primary or secondary market research. Primary research data is obtained by approaching the source directly, such as via telephone or in-person surveys, or focus groups. Secondary market research is conducted by a research firm or third party organization, and the data is available for sale or sometimes for free, through the government or over the Internet.

The best way to understand customers is to talk to them- real people in the real world. This is the best type of primary market research. Customers are human, and even in business to business marketing, individual buying behavior varies significantly. There are several ways to study real customers. The easiest thing to do is to go through your contact list and talk to your friends and colleagues who work in other companies. Do informal surveys by phone to get information on how people might use or judge a product, or what their business problems might be. You can also get a lot of information from your direct sales force, because they are in constant contact with existing and potential customers. You can conduct focus groups and surveys with potential customers. You can do road shows for existing customers to obtain direct feedback for future products. And during the launch phase, the most powerful customer input is what you learn during a beta testing phase.

Secondary market research is available for sale through various market research companies and organizations, such as Gartner Group, Forrester Research, Yankee Group, Frost and Sullivan, IDC, and many others. Most of these organizations have websites where they make some of their report summaries available free of charge in order to stimulate sales of their more complete reports and research services. These market research studies are usually focused on specific technologies or industry segments, but they usually contain much useful information about buying behavior, customer needs, and market demand.

For business to consumer marketing, demographic data may be helpful. Demographic data describes statistics about a target customer population. Several factors can be measured about people, including geographic location, age, gender, family size, educational level, income level, purchase history, and preferences. This type of data is gathered by market research firms as well as by the government. You may notice such surveys attached to product registration and warranty cards. Many surveys are conducted by telemarketing or in person at retail locations such as shopping malls. Some information is also available over the Internet, and can be found through routine web searches.

Trade publications also publish articles that contain market research on customers. These are also partially available for free over the Internet, or through paid subscriptions to the specific publications.

In general, the Internet has made much customer research data accessible. It is much easier to find secondary market research data, and the Internet is also used as a vehicle to collect more customer data. There are more ways than ever to find accurate and current information about your potential customers.

Customer profile

Now that you've studied your customers, and you know everything about them, you should develop a summary profile. Here's a sample list of customer attributes for a business-to-business product:

-Title, relative position in organization
-Job responsibilities
-Gender, if appropriate
-Purchase authority or influence over purchase decisions
-How buying decisions are made
-Buying history and frequency for similar products
-Business problem that needs to be solved
-How the product will be used
-Business benefits of the product
-Value to customers, and price they would pay

Once you have this list, then the next step is to determine how many customers are out there that have a similar profile, in order to determine the market size and trends. The next chapter addresses how to characterize your market from the information you have gathered about your customers.

5

Market Analysis

The primary objective of product launch is to prepare the market for your product. It is imperative that you have a good understanding of the market size, trends, and conditions as you prepare to launch. Your product was probably designed for a certain target market; however, market conditions change rapidly, and an updated market analysis is needed during the launch phase. This updated analysis will help you make decisions about the launch date and the timing of marketing programs, advertising, and public relations campaigns. Sometimes market conditions can change so much that launches are postponed or even cancelled. Assessing the market size and trends also helps to identify the optimum marketing programs that you will need to introduce your product and get your target customers to buy.

It is important to develop a thorough characterization of your target market segment(s) before studying them in detail. This market segment characterization defines the target market for the launch. Your target market will have several different attributes. These include market size (current and future), market dynamics (trends). You also may have a target market share identified. Solid market analysis is a vital part of the launch process, to ensure that the proper venues for reaching your customers can be established, using product messages that they will hear and understand.

Market segments

A market segment is a portion of a larger market. Many different criteria are used to define market segments, such as industry, geographic factors, consumer versus business-to-business, technologies, or customer demographics. Some companies define market segments as horizontal (cutting across several different industries), or vertical (one industry). You may have one or more market segments that you want to target for your product. These market segments may already be established, or they may be entirely new to the company.

Vertical markets are related to an industry, such as banking, transportation, telecommunications, medical, or manufacturing. It may be that your company has sold many products into a specific industry, and your company has built up specific knowledge of the customer problems and needs that are unique to that industry. Companies often use the market segment that they are most familiar with to launch their new products, as long as the existing customers have a need for the product. In this way, companies can leverage their industry knowledge. If the vertical market is new to your company, then a different market entry strategy may be required. This could mean anything from channel marketing, to advertising campaigns, to attending new trade shows, or creating entirely new marketing literature. This can be a very expensive proposition, so any new target segments should be identified as soon as possible, so that the resources can be allocated appropriately.

Horizontal markets cut across all types of industries and businesses. For example, products that have basic functionality that any business can use represent an opportunity to target a horizontal market. Examples of products that are sold in a horizontal market are personal computers, anti-virus software, and telecommunications equipment. Such products might be customizable by the end user customer, but they are sold in a basic configuration. Another way to characterize a horizontal market is by identifying a type of individual who has the same organizational function in any company, such as an accountant, a CEO, or an IT manager. For horizontal markets, the description of the product user or the type of company will be high-level and more generalized than that of a vertical market.

Consumer markets can be horizontal or vertical. Vertical segments might be based on demographic information, such as senior citizens, women over 30, teenagers, or low-income families. A horizontal consumer market includes all types of consumers, regardless of demographics.

Vertical and horizontal markets may be global or restricted to specific geographies. When vertical markets are also global, country and cultural boundaries can create smaller segments within a segment. Product functionality may differ in some countries, as well as how customers use the product in business or consumer applications. These differences may represent smaller market segments.

Once you have determined your market segment or segments, you need to take a look at the market size and trends that affect that segment. If you are studying several vertical markets, it may require more research in many different publications in order to find out the trends. The more specifically you define your segments and the customers in your segment, the easier it will be to develop marketing messages that will get their attention.

Conducting market analysis

The best way to find meaningful market information is to stay focused on your target market segment, and to read the news and articles that are written about doing business in that segment. Figure 5.1 is a suggested list of sources.

-Trade journals, business magazines: articles about trends in technology, economy and business

-Analyst reports and publications: predictions of market size and trends by technology, industry, type of customer

-Company websites: recent news, press releases, annual reports or earnings reports

-Financial newspapers and media: earnings reports and news

-Your company's databases: changes in sales for existing products, type and number of new customers, sales leads by geographic location

-Market surveys and research reports: specific trends and size estimates with demographic information

Figure 5.1 Where to Look and What to Look For

The more detailed your focus, the more useful the data will be in terms of identifying the real trends that affect the market demand. There are many different types of trends that may be relevant to your market. For example, trends can measure whether a market is growing and why, they can predict the rates at which technologies are adopted, or they can describe the new business models that companies are using to sell into the market.

You should look for overall demand in your target market and how it is changing. Demand my increase, decrease, or stay flat in response to various economic or technology changes. Look for the reasons behind the fluctuations in demand. You also need to consider how fast your market is changing in terms of demand, new customers, and rate of technology adoption. It's important to capture the basis for your estimates so that you can justify your numbers later on to the decision-makers.

Validating the market analysis

Just because it is written, it isn't necessarily so. You should take the time to validate the predictions or forecasts found in media publications with real people in your market segment, in other words, your target customer. Very often, trade journals are written on the basis of one or two examples that support the prediction, and they might not reflect the rest of the market segment. Also, if the market is brand new, it is even more critical to validate the information.

You will have information about your customer from your customer characterization (see Chapter 4). To validate the market trends and size, you should compare the target customer profile with the individuals in the target market segment to identify the individuals who most closely match your customer description. You should then speak with such individuals from the market segment to find out if they have the same problem that needs to be solved, similar value propositions, and comparable buying behavior. If they do, then the market trends and estimated size will be more reliable measures of your real target market. There are many ways to conduct this validation, as listed in Figure 5.2.

-Network and talk to colleagues

-Conduct surveys with real or
    potential customers

-Do focus groups

-Contract with a market research
    firm for a specific study

-Hire a consultant with expertise
    in your target market

-Develop a prototype or demo
    and obtain customer feedback

Figure 5.2 Ways to Validate Market Trends and Size

Market size projections

Before your product was developed, there were probably some projections made about how large the market would be at the time of product launch. Usually these projections are expressed in dollars over a certain period of time or for a specific calendar year. If those projections are still available, it's a good idea to review them before you update the market size. Sometimes, such information is taken from a published report or article, and it may be possible to contact the source of the data for an update.

Market size is usually expressed in terms of dollars, numbers of people, or product units. There are several measures of market size:

-Total available market (TAM)
-Served available market (SAM)
-Share of market (SOM)

You should use all three measures in analyzing your market.

Total available market is the total dollar volume that customers in the market would pay for goods and service, over some unit of time (number of years or specific calendar year). Depending on the product, this number can be in the millions or billions. Here's an example:

Over the next two years, the total market size for broadband services will exceed $200 billion.

On the surface, a total available market that is in the billions may seem very attractive. Who wouldn't want to enter this market? However, this estimate pertains to all broadband services, which could include anything from basic connectivity, to security, to networks, to technical support. How much of that market would be available to you (SAM)? It's likely to be a much smaller number. The most meaningful use of total available market numbers is to examine the trend over a period of years, or market dynamics. If it is a growing market, then that is a very positive indicator for your product. Sometimes these trends are described using a compounded annual growth rate. Any rate that exceeds 10% per year is usually regarded as a fast-growing market.

Applying market trend information

Market trends will help you forecast market size going into the future, and to help you estimate the other measures of market size, such as served available market. Market trends are described in many different ways. Sometimes they reflect relative demand for certain types of products, and in that situation the trend is more related to adoption rate of technology, or the pace at which technology solutions are evolving. The sample market size statement above regarding broadband is a technology demand trend. Another type of trend statement refers to customer problems and contains a projection on how many customers are likely to have that problem. Here's an example:

> *With the increasing trend of insider security threats in large companies, more security controls will be required for outbound network traffic. By the end of the decade, 40% of all companies will integrate additional security hardware and software into their network infrastructure.*

Trends are sometimes stated in relative terms, comparing regions or technologies:

> *Markets for wireless communications equipment are growing faster outside the United States, particularly in Asia.*

Trends also can reflect widespread changes in business processes in companies:

> *Over the next two years, the adoption of network-based business applications will continue. As a result, IT organizations will need to integrate more cross-functional business processes into the design of the network infrastructure.*

Trends are based on observations of business, technology, and overall market dynamics, and they contain an element of predicting the future. Studying trends can help you piece together what industry experts think about the demand for your product, and how the demand is expected to change in the future. For example, assume that you are launching a software product that is designed for wireless broadband communications. Considered together, two of the above examples would indicate that there is a large and growing total market for your product, and maybe in Asia. Senior management generally requires validation that the market dynamics at the time of launch indicate that the market is still large and growing before they will allow the launch to go forward. Once you have verified this, the next step is to identify what part of that large market you need to target.

Estimating Served Available Market (SAM)

Take a look at your customer profile. How many customers are there in the total available market that would fit this profile? Let's assume that you are selling a software package that enables companies to monitor email server performance. You have determined that the customer who will buy your product is an IT manager or network administrator. If your total available market estimate includes all server software products, then you would need to determine what portion of that total might pertain to email servers, or possibly, how many companies have dedicated email servers. In further research of market trends, you find an estimate of the number of enterprises who have dedicated email servers. That number would then represent your served available market. This is an estimate of the market size that you can serve with your product solution, and the number is driven by the specifics of your solution. For instance, companies who don't have dedicated email servers would probably not be interested in buying your product.

Estimating Share of Market (SOM)

At this point of the analysis, you need to calculate one more market size number. You need to decide what percentage of the served available market you want to target and maintain; that is, market share.

Sometimes market share is driven by capacity. There may be hundreds or thousands of customers in your target segment, but your ability to deliver products to everyone is limited. You may choose a small percentage as your short-term goal, with potential to grow the market share later as you build sales.

More often, market share depends on competition. Having few competitors might mean that you aim for a larger market share. Having many competitors might mean that the market is fragmented, and no one company owns more than a small percentage of the market.

Target market characterization

Now that you have determined your total available market, served available market, and market share, you have a reasonable characterization of your market size. This is sometimes called the TAM-SAM-SOM analysis and is represented in a bar graph as shown in Figure 5.3. The TAM is gradually reduced in size to arrive at the most realistic estimate of market share, based on trends, competitive analysis, and capacity to deliver.

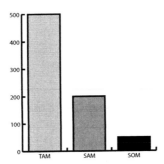

Figure 5.3 TAM-SAM-SOM Chart

The SOM estimate can be displayed on a bar chart by year to illustrate how your market share will grow, as shown in Figure 5.4. To compile this chart, you will also need to obtain sales projections for the product to be launched.

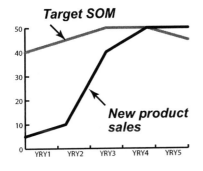

-How will you ramp up sales
 to reach your target SOM
 before demand peaks?

-Will you have to ramp up
 quickly to stay ahead of
 the competition?

Figure 5.4 Growth of Market Share Over Time

Once both curves are plotted on this chart, it can be very enlightening in terms of expectations for the product being launched. If there is a steep upward sales curve as on this example, there may a lot of pressure to obtain early sales and capture market share more quickly. That may create a need to launch the product earlier or create more aggressive external marketing programs in order to realize the sales goals.

You may have more than one segment that you are targeting. You should develop a market size estimate for each segment. Market size estimates are important for launch because they will help determine priorities of various marketing programs and allocate budgets. A larger market segment may require more communication vehicles to build product awareness than a small market segment.

Along with the market size estimates, you need to describe the market segments in more detail. Using your customer profile, extend the description across your market segment. Where will you find these customers? What type of company or industry? These characterizations will be used to develop the right marketing programs to create awareness of your product in each target segment. Your target customers may attend industry-specific trade shows or read trade publications targeted for their industry segment. The detailed characterization is important because it helps you to target venues for advertising and to develop press tours. Messages in marketing literature may need to be targeted for applications that are unique to your customer's business environment. The more information that you can gather about customers and their market segment, the more effective your marketing campaign will be in reaching them.

In the next chapter, you will learn how to study and monitor competition so that you can effectively position your product in your target market.

6

Competition

At the beginning of a product cycle, when the original product idea is developed, it is tempting to think that there are no competitors out there who will get to market before you do. However, real life is such that by the time the product emerges from the hibernation of the development cycle, competitors have indeed materialized and sometimes they already have some market share - in your target market! In the world of high technology, competition is one thing you can always count on. It is critical to constantly monitor your competition: past, current, and potential. Knowing your competitors will help you better position your product in the market, enabling you to highlight the product features and functions that are different than your competitors' products. And at the time of press release, this knowledge will help prepare you for answering questions that the trade press or analysts may ask about your competitors.

Identifying your competitors

How do you stack up against the competition? First, you need to know who your competitors are. It's easy to say, "Oh, yeah, it's the same old guys we always compete with." There is danger in being complacent; your competitors are not standing still, waiting for you to announce your next product. You constantly need to monitor what they are doing, and be on the lookout for new entrants in your market space. New companies start operations every day, especially in high tech markets. Assume you will always have new competitors to worry about.

Make a list of the competitors that you will analyze. List the companies that already sell products that have the same functionality as yours, the "known" competitors. Next, list the companies who sell many other types of products to your existing market segment or segments but who don't have a product that has the same functionality as yours. You need to consider companies who sell diverse products to your target market as potential competitors because they may have a "portfolio" strategy to develop products, and may have the technological potential to bring a competing product to the market quickly. Also consider your target customer's current solution or alternative ways the customer can solve their problem without buying your product. Figure 6.1 shows the various types of competitors that should be considered:

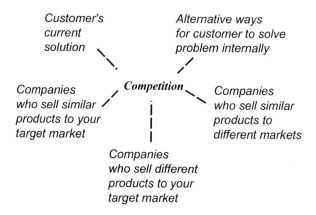

Figure 6.1 Types of Competitors

Levels of competition – the competitive environment

When evaluating the competition, companies usually start looking at the companies and products first, but it's a good idea to start at a higher level by examining the competitive environment. If your business is an established company with several product lines, you already have a lot of knowledge about your competitors for the existing products. When you are preparing to launch a new product (especially to a new target market), you should not simply assume that you would be dealing with the same old competitors. Any time you make even a subtle change to product functionality or features, it creates the possibility that there might be other companies out there who could develop something identical to it, and they may no be in your market space yet. That's why it's imperative to revisit the competitive environment when you're getting ready to launch a new product. Evaluate the competitive environment with "new eyes". Figure 6.2 shows the various types of competitive environments that might apply to your situation:

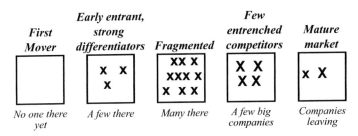

Figure 6.2 The Five Competitive Environments

These different environments reflect the number and size of companies currently competing in them. Sometimes your new product is poised to be the first to market (First-mover). That's both good news and bad news. The good news is that you will get the attention and have the opportunity to set a standard, on your way to being market share leader. The bad news is that everyone will be coming after you and trying to take market share away. Are you prepared to allocate the resources to sustain and defend your position, beginning with the first launch?

The next two environments, Early entrant and Fragmented, require strong differentiation from your competitors in order to be successful. For launch, this means that the key messages must relate closely to the differentiators and be communicated effectively. The environment with a few entrenched competitors present a challenge for new entrants because you will have to take market share away from an incumbent by offering the customer more choices and clear differentiators. Launching a product into that environment may require more of an awareness campaign, followed by more targeted marketing materials that highlight those choices. The fifth environment, the Mature market, means that companies are leaving the market due to financial or technological reasons or that innovation is no longer present and it has become a commodity market. Launching a product into a mature market is a challenge because it's more difficult to get customers excited about the product.

Knowing the competitive environment before launch can help determine the go-to-market strategy for the launch, and it can also help in planning the extent and nature of external marketing programs required to be successful.

Levels of competition – the company and product

Competitors are normally defined as other companies that sell products similar to yours to customers in similar markets. Traditional competitive analysis used to focus only on price and performance of your products versus the competitors' products. It's not so simple any more. Many other factors make a difference in how you measure up to your competitors. Criteria such as customer support levels, compliance with evolving standards, customized solutions, choice of strategic partners, number of distribution channels, reputation in specific markets, financial health of the company, and continuous product migration strategies are all important in distinguishing you from your competitors. In general, competitors can make life difficult for you at two levels: the product level and the company level.

Competitive analysis at the product level is more common. Here the focus is on the features and functions of similar products and how they compare to yours. Product level analysis is very important, because it will help you identify the primary differences between products and enable you to highlight the unique advantages of your product for your potential customers.

As a company, a competitor has business strategies in place, and has goals for marketing, finance, and operational performance. Sometimes, companies compete well and become market leaders because they are very well run, and they achieve or surpass their business goals, independent of their products' reputation in the marketplace. In this way, competitors might be a serious threat to you at the company level. As part of competitive analysis, it is important to evaluate competing companies and how they have been performing with regard to general business criteria such as profitability, growth, or strategy, along with their general reputation in the industry. Figure 6.3 lists the major attributes that should be considered at a company and product level:

Company Level	Product Level
-Financial health -Company history -Size (revenues, employees) -Public or private -Strategic partners -Market reputation -Brand strength	-Features/functions -Price -Sales history -Customer success stories -Product history -Number, type of products -Familiarity with target customer

Figure 6.3 Key Competitor Attributes to Consider

It is important to be armed with information about your competitors at both levels, so that you can position your product and company messages in the best possible way to develop awareness of your product and generate sales.

Analyzing the competition

Studying your competitors is important, and there are many ways to get information about them. The proliferation of corporate websites has greatly facilitated competitive analysis. If you know what to look for and how to analyze the content, you can obtain a lot of information about your existing and potential competitors just by carefully reading their websites. This is called the gathering of competitive intelligence, or "e-telligence".

You may have heard of reverse engineering. Well, this process is sort of like reverse marketing. By reading web content, you can identify the company's key marketing messages, and therefore you can figure out what their key differentiators are and much, much more. And then you'll have some ideas on how to change your strategy or your product in order to be more competitive. It will also help tremendously to go through this exercise right before a launch when you are updating the competitive analysis.

In order to figure out where to find the competitor's secrets, let's first consider the sections of a typical corporate website. Companies may organize the information a little differently, but here are the basic sections and what they usually contain:

Homepage: Company logo, description of what company does, news, navigation bars listing sections, search box

Company: history, management team, jobs, locations and contact information

Press Room or Media: current and archived press releases, press contacts

Products and Services: lists or groups of key products and services the company offers

Events: trade shows, user groups or other key industry events where the company will have a presence

Support: information on how and where to obtain technical support and customer service

Investors (if a public company): latest SEC reports and filings, quarterly results, contact information for investment packets

Partners: list of existing partners, applications for becoming a partner

Links and Ads: hot links to affiliates' websites

Each of the sections that follow describes what to look for and the significance of what you may find there. You can analyze the sections in any order. A good way to accumulate the information is to print out one page from each section, and then highlight the information, adding a word or two that describe the significance. You may also write questions in the margins, such as "growth through product lines or hiring?" These questions may prompt you to look for other clues in other pages and sections of the website as you read through it.

Homepage

This is the page that's all about image. Look at the basic layout of the page. Is there a lot of text or a combination of text and graphics? If it's too busy with too much information, it may mean the company is highly technical and detail-oriented. Is it sleek and modern looking with a minimum of text but lots of headings and other links? This says to the visitor: we have a clear mission and vision, we are organized, and we see the big picture.

What types of graphics are on the homepage; are there pictures of people or of technology and products? If there are people, what are they doing; are they using the technology in some way or are they just happy and smiling? When companies use lots of people pictures, they are trying to identify with customers and say that people are very important to them. That may or may not be true in the way that the company does business, but it does mean that they realize the importance of customers as people. If there are only pictures of products and technology, it can mean that the company has a very technical focus.

The last thing to consider on the homepage is what you notice first on the page; what draws your eye? It may be a flashing icon for a new product, or it might be a colorful banner listing the latest company news, or it might be a prominent mission statement near the top of the page. Whatever is most prominent is usually the key information that the company wants the site visitor to know. If it's a news item or new product that's prominent, that says the company is not stagnant, but is moving forward and growing. If it's the mission statement, that means the company wants to establish and reinforce its reputation in the marketplace.

Company

The company culture and organizational structure will be described in this section of the website. Most companies of any size have a brief company history, which tells you how long the company has been in business. The longer it's been in business, the more stable the company will be, but it also may mean that the company is not in a growth cycle. Younger companies may be in growth mode and can be more aggressive in the marketplace until they are established and stable. The company history may also indicate whether the company has been involved in mergers and acquisitions. If that has occurred within the past year, the company may still be in transition mode, which can be distracting for companies until everyone is reassigned and established in their new jobs. That's also when a company might be most vulnerable in terms of competitive position in the marketplace. Is it time to make your move?

The job listings are often listed in the Company section as well. What types of positions are open; are they in engineering, research and development, marketing, accounting, or sales? Many job listings are indicators of growth cycles. Technical jobs can indicate that the company is developing new products. Sales jobs can mean that they are expanding geographically.

The key part of the Company is the management team, sometimes called "executive leadership" or "executive team". There are usually bios and sometimes photos of senior management. The first thing to consider is which titles of executives are listed. Are they all technical titles? That may mean that the company is technology-driven and not market-driven. Are there lots of sales titles, especially with geographic locations listed? That indicates the degree of global presence that the company has and also where they want to achieve sales growth. Read through the bios to find out where the executives have worked before. They may have worked for other competitors in your industry, bringing with them valuable contacts with key customers. Does that give them an edge? Also look at their background and education. Do they bring unique expertise that will make that company a stronger competitor?

Press Room or Media

Read a few of the current press releases. They will address the hot products, people, and issues for which the company hopes to get media coverage. Press releases make a statement to the industry that the company is an important player (whether they are or not). When you read the press releases, what is the emphasis; people, technology, customer successes? If it's a press release about a person, read the information as you would an executive bio. Adding that person to the company may be a key competitive move for them. Press releases are usually done before and during a major product launch, so that media coverage can help to create awareness of the new product about to be released. What are they saying about the new product or technology? That will give you an indication about their next product that you'll be competing against. If the press release contains a key quote or endorsement from one of their customers, who is the customer and are they part of your target market? If so, that may have an impact on your market campaign.

Products and Services

This is usually the biggest section of any website, and there may be many different pages grouped together. If there are lots of product categories, you can read through them and get a sense for how the company creates and develops their long-term product roadmap. How often do they add new features or whole new products to a product line? How different is each product from the previous product? How long do they keep each product available? How do they group their product families? If the company in question has been successful and has a big share of the market, they are probably letting market demand drive their product roadmap, which should be a good plan to follow for your company as well.

Events

Wondering whether the competitor will be at the next key trade show? Well, here you will find out. Companies will usually list a booth number for a trade show, along with any key presentations that will be given by their executives. If your company doesn't participate in that trade show, perhaps you need to consider it. Other events besides trade shows might be listed as well, such as company-sponsored user conferences. Take a look at the invitation or application to join their user group and what's involved. Sometimes they will state how many people belong to the group. That will give you an idea of the size of their customer base. You may not get much further than that, however, unless you fill in the online application, and as a competitor, they are not likely to let you in!

Support

Companies usually want to make a good impression with potential customers that they have superior customer service, so this section usually addresses the availability and quality of their technical support and/or customer service. Read what they say about the their support and then figure out what you have to do in order to provide similar services.

Investors

Public companies usually will have their SEC documents and latest annual reports available for download from their websites. Downloading and reading these can give you a lot more detailed information about planned growth, sales by product and division, executive bios and salaries, and operating information.

Partners

Some companies will have their partners' company logos posted prominently somewhere on the site, especially if the partner is large or well known. Sometimes these partners are in place because the company depends on them to provide complementary products and services to their customers in order to deliver the "whole product". Just because you may not have similar partners doesn't necessarily mean it's a bad thing; you may not need them. Still, it's important to understand the competitor's partner relationships and why they are in place. If you need one in the future, that may limit your choices.

Links and Ads

The presence of links to other websites are telling because they must be important enough to the company that they risk having a site visitor click away from the company site to go somewhere else. There had better be a good business reason! Sometimes companies have business arrangements such as commissions, and sometimes they are merely business partners and they have agreed to do co-marketing between their websites. You should take note of these links and try to understand why the business relationship exists - what is the benefit to the competitor? Might your company have a good reason to do something similar?

Other websites that yield considerable information about competitors are the market research and industry analyst organizations, such as Gartner Group, Forrester, Yankee Group, IDC, and Frost and Sullivan. Some of this information is on a subscription basis only, but occasionally there is some limited information available free of charge that can help with competitive analysis.

Use web search engines to find articles about companies in trade journals and industry newspapers. Search for the most current information (current month or two), but also read information in the previous twelve months. You may find patterns of your competitors' product strategies if you look at what they are announcing over a longer period of time.

Competitive matrix

What makes your company different from your competitor? What are the differences between your product and your competitors' products? The best way to organize the information from your analysis is to construct a simple matrix chart or a spreadsheet. At the top of the first column, put the name of your company. The other columns will have competitors' names at the top. Add a subheading called "Company-level". Below this subheading, list the strengths of your company, and then the weaknesses. How does your company compare to the competitor? Do you pay more attention to customer support? Do you have multiple distribution channels to reach your customer? Have you recently acquired another company, adding to your technological or financial capabilities? Add this information to the matrix for your company, and then do a line by line comparison for your competitors for each of your strengths and also your weaknesses. When you have filled in the columns for the company level information, then add a subheading called "Product Level".

Using the product features and functions that you developed when you defined your product (Chapter 2), list those features and functions in the left-most column.

Complete the matrix, line by line. This gives you a comprehensive comparison chart to easily identify the differences between your product and competitors' products. Sometimes, a single feature or function will pop out that no one else has. You need to highlight that line in the matrix. That is a key differentiator that needs to be emphasized through the positioning and then the messaging for the product.

On the next page is an example of a matrix for a network router, with three major competitors.

My company	Competitor A	Competitor B	Competitor C
Company level:			
Strong system integration partners	System integration group part of company	Have consulting and systems integration group	Reputation for mismanaging system integration
Product migration strategy in place	"Me too" products; not innovative	Focus is on customization and services, not products	Product strategy is modularity
Mixed market focus; small to large companies	Focus on small to medium businesses	Focus on large enterprise customers	Unknown market strategy
Product level:			
Compatible with 10 protocols	Compatible with 6 protocols	Compatible with 10 protocols	Compatible with 6 protocols
Scalable to 24 ports	Scalable to 16 ports	Scalable to 24 ports	Scalable to 16 ports
Modular configuration; can add units	Fixed, customized configuration	Expandable only through customization	Sold only in minimum configuration
Integrated test software	Integrated test software	Integrated test software	Must purchase test software
Price: $4000 per module	Varies with customization	$3000 base price for standard model	$2000 per module

For this example, the differentiators at the company level are end-to-end business solutions and strong product migration strategy (first and second rows). At the product level, differentiators are protocol support and modular configuration (fourth and sixth rows in the table).

Features, advantages, and benefits

Now that you have identified the differentiators at the product level and the company level, the next step is to define the customer benefits of your product or service. The way to do this is to construct another matrix, a features-advantages-benefits chart, or "FAB" chart. There are three columns in this chart. The first column lists the product features that were also differentiators from your competitive matrix. For each feature, the "advantage" column contains a description of how the feature or function is different or better than the competitors' products. The third column lists the customer benefit of that product feature; what does that feature do to help solve their business problem or give them added value? Once this FAB chart is filled in for all the differentiators, it forms the basis for your detailed product positioning analysis and will help you craft marketing messages for the product.

Now, we put it all together. Taking our example, your product differentiators are protocol support and modularity. Your company differentiators are defined product migration strategy and end to end business solutions. The scalability differentiator is an advantage because none of the other competitors offer as much scalability in the number of ports. It's a benefit to the customer because it means investment protection; there is "room for expansion" and the company won't outgrow this product quickly. In similar fashion, the other three differentiators are described, and the business benefits for the customer are noted. The FAB chart for this example would look like the table on the following page.

Features	Advantages	Benefits
Product migration strategy	Offers a series of products to fit different needs of businesses; in the product business	Customers have more choices of products, and assurances that they will have future products that meet their needs
End to end solution	Can serve more markets than other competitors	As businesses grow, there are more solutions available to choose from
Protocol Support	Compatible with more protocols than other competing products	Customer can link multiprotocol network traffic without having to buy additional systems
Modularity	Each module is scalable and has better price to performance ratio than competing products	Customers only need to buy enough modules to fit current business needs, and can modules as their business grows

Once this chart is complete, it can then be used to guide the strategy and positioning analysis and the development of key messages. That process is described in Chapters 8 and 9.

Now that you have a good understanding of your target market and how your product and company stack up against the competition, you need to address distribution, which defines how you will get your product to that market.

7

Distribution Plan

Much as a river cuts channels as it spreads out over a flood-plain, distribution channels provide a means to get your product to its ultimate destination: your customer. A business model map is a diagram that shows all the business entities involved in getting your product to your customer. These business entities include your company, your customer, your suppliers and distribution channels. A business model map looks like a flow chart; an example is presented as Figure 7.1. Business model mapping is an effective planning tool for product launch because it helps you to understand the external environment and to identify the business relationships that will be in place when the product is ready to launch.

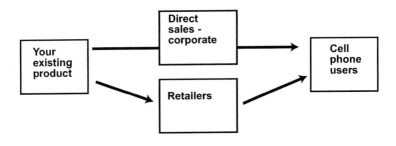

Figure 7.1 Business Model for a Wireless Phone Company

The business model map will help clarify which entities you must interface with in order to implement the launch. In the case of Figure 7.1, you will need to involve the direct sales force and the retail distributors when the launch is implemented. Sometimes there are also suppliers involved, as shown in Figure 7.2, a business model for a PDA:

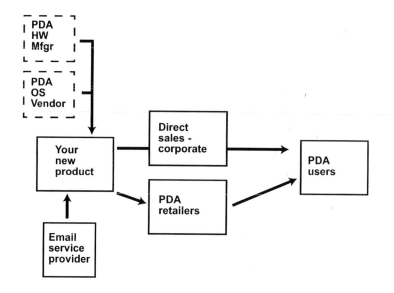

Figure 7.2 Business Model Map with Supply Chain

Supply chain partners often add unique technological value to your product or bring specific brand recognition that can enhance your external marketing campaign during launch. Therefore, it's important to find out as much as possible about all entities in the business model.

Sometimes at the beginning of the launch cycle, there is a need to identify new distribution channels for the product that's being launched. Business model maps can also be used for comparing channel candidates. Figure 7.3 illustrates the comparison of two different channels. You can evaluate the tradeoffs of doing business with different channels. What discount must you extend to do business with them? How much revenue are they likely to generate? How effective will they be at reaching your market and increasing your market share? Comparisons can easily be made by mapping in the dollars and then deciding which candidate will be more effective.

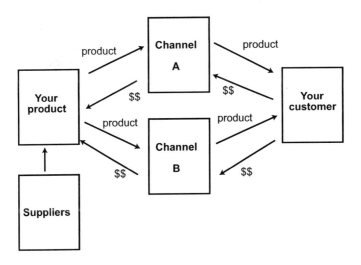

Figure 7.3 Using a Business Model to Choose the
Best Channel Partner

What are channels?

There are many different ways to get the product to your customer. Distribution channels can involve many different types of organizations, ranging from your own company's direct sales force to other companies such as resellers, strategic partners, developers, systems integrators, distributors, wholesalers, retailers, catalog houses, and original equipment manufacturers or OEMs.

In general, channels may be classified as direct or indirect. Direct means that you have employees of your company who are selling your company's products directly to your customers. A direct sales force is the most common channel used by companies; some refer to their sales force as "the channel", implying that there is only one. Indirect channels are other companies, organizations or individuals who sell your product to your customer. A transfer must take place to get your product to your channel, so that they can in turn get the product to your customer. Because there is an entity in between your company and the customer, the channel is called indirect.

Channel marketing is very important in a product launch. As was explained in the Chapter 1, the launch phase is when the market is prepared for your product. You must prepare all of the people involved in getting your product into the market, and that includes direct and indirect channels. They need to be armed with as much information as possible so that they have all the knowledge required to convince the customer to buy your product, resulting in revenue for your company.

One of the most difficult things about channel marketing is the need to get detailed information to the channels well in advance of the launch. Sales representatives do not like surprises and should not hear about your new product from their customer instead of you! Indirect and direct sales representatives need to be prepared to sell your product well before your product is announced publicly. This means that channel marketing materials and sales collateral needs to be developed before some of the other marketing programs, and this needs to be built into the launch schedule once the announcement date has been determined.

Channels need education, information, and selling tools for your product. It is not as simple as merely placing an ad and assuming that the channels will have enough information. Channel marketing programs sometimes resemble detailed training programs, with specific information on how to sell the product and how to find the right customers. The material needed for this type of program can be voluminous. You may need to provide customized marketing information that is traditionally used in a specific channel or industry; this may involve repackaging and reformatting your basic product marketing information. Just as you need to target marketing materials to get your customer's attention, so must you target the marketing information for the intermediary: your channel. In a way, this is a two-pronged approach to marketing; you must sell to the channel and then give them the proper tools to sell to the customer. This also means that you must fully understand the channel, their selling operations, and their relationship to your company.

During the launch phase, it is important to plan marketing programs for existing channels as well as for those new channels that might be in the process of development by your company. Sometimes, channel arrangements and contracts will be put into place within a few months of launch. If so, it is helpful to have this knowledge in advance so that you can have some materials ready when the business relationship begins. Depending on the timing of these arrangements relative to the product announcement date, pre-launch marketing materials may also be required.

Direct channels

The direct channel is your company's sales force. Most companies spend a considerable amount of money educating the sales force and keeping them up to date. It is essential for their job to have as much product information as possible, so that they can meet their personal sales objectives along with the company's goals. The sales force should be at the top of the list in terms of who gets product marketing information.

It's also important to understand the selling structure of your company. Find out if your sales force is on a commission basis or some incentive arrangement for specific product lines. If the sales force has less of an incentive to sell your product than other company products, you may not need to develop as much marketing material. However, if they are highly incentivized to sell your product versus others, they may want more information as well as guidelines from the product development organization on how best to sell the product that is being launched.

You need to know how the sales organization operates. What does the organization chart look like, and how many managers are there? How do they communicate and who distributes information to them? Do they meet as a group quarterly or on a regular basis? Because sales representatives would prefer to spend their work day in front of customers, trying to make sales, they will have limited time for sales training and for reading new marketing material. Most sales organizations of any size have coordinators or managers who work with the sales representatives to get information to them. You need to identify the proper contact person and find out what types of material the sales force needs for new products, as well as the most effective means of getting the information to them. Because sales people travel constantly, intranet or web-based communication is used extensively for marketing information. When they don't have ready access to email or the Internet, CD-based material also works well. Whatever form of information is most portable or mobile will be the most useful for the sales force.

Marketing materials for the sales force

Usually, the sales force receives different marketing materials than you would give to your customers. Sales people need to know the confidential information about the product: the company's strategic objectives for the product, as well as competitive analysis information. This is obviously not the type of information that would be given to a customer. In addition to this company-internal information, sales people need to see the marketing collateral that will be given to the customer. They also need sales presentations that are preformatted and ready to present to customers, along with sales tools such as product reference guides, configuration guides if applicable to the product, and product selection tools that will help them do their job more effectively. Marketing material for the direct sales force quite often will represent the largest piece of the launch budget, because of specialized materials that need to be created.

You will need to know how the sales force is organized and distributed geographically. Are they organized by territories, regions, countries, or by vertical markets? If sales representatives are assigned to specific vertical markets, they may need specialized marketing collateral that is tailored to these markets. If there are sales representatives in other countries, the marketing material may need to be translated. Also, foreign business cultures often dictate the types of collateral that is used, and you will need to plan for that as well.

Is there a sales training group inside the company that focuses on conducting regular training sessions for the sales force? If so, you may need to create one or more presentations on the product being launched, as well as to coordinate with the training group regarding the timing of the training. It is desirable to train the sales force well before the announcement date for the product. If the timing does not work out, it will be necessary to find some other means to "pre-launch" the product to the sales force until they can be trained in person. Find the support organization for the direct sales force, and get them involved on the launch team so that they will be up to date on what's coming and can make suggestions as to the optimum marketing materials. It's also a good idea to have a sales representative on the launch team if you can convince him or her to make some time to participate. Because sales representatives have current customer knowledge, they can contribute a great deal of information on how to formulate effective messages for customers and which marketing materials work best.

Indirect channels

There are many different types of indirect channels, and each type operates differently. Value-added resellers and systems integrators are in the business of selling services along with products, and they usually need a variety of products from different vendors in order to offer their customers the maximum amount of choice. Developers usually create software applications for hardware platforms or chips and use other software in the process; they sell integrated hardware and software or just software to their customers. Distributors and wholesalers sell many different types of products and need to sell virtually all vendors' products in every product category in order to serve their customers. Retail and catalog sales most often sell to consumers but also sell to businesses, and like distributors, they need to carry a wide variety of products from different vendors. OEMs buy products and create larger, more complex products that they in turn sell to their customers. Strategic partners can include any type of company that has a business relationship with your company to do joint product development, marketing, or sales. What all of these types of channels have in common is that their primary business focus is not on your company's product. This means that you must market to them first, before you can get them to sell your product to their customers.

Marketing programs for indirect channels

Because of their nature, indirect channels require marketing programs that are slightly different from programs developed for direct channels. This is because indirect channels are not employees of your company and sell other people's products alongside yours. Your objective is to get their attention and incentivize them to sell your product instead of your competitor's product. For effective channel marketing programs, it is important to focus on key differentiators in order to clearly distinguish your product. There are several steps that need to be taken in order to identify the right marketing programs and materials for indirect channels.

The first step is to develop a clear understanding of each indirect channel's business operations and organizational structure. Most companies have an organization to develop and manage channels, and you should meet with your company's channel management to learn all you can about the indirect channels. For each indirect channel, determine what the selling environment is like. The sales representatives for your indirect channels may or may not be organized like those of your own sales force; they may be organized by market or region. You need to be aware of how they are organized so that you can tailor marketing materials to fit their needs. They may also have one or more account representatives assigned to your company whose job it is to distribute marketing materials to the sales representatives.

You must identify which factors the channel sales representatives use in deciding which product to recommend or promote in each selling situation. Each type of indirect channel will be different in that regard, and you need to get as much information as you can about how the channel sales representatives make those decisions. The company acting as an indirect channel for you must fulfill their own customer's needs; that is their first priority. If your product will fit that into that solution, then you need to supply them with the information that will highlight the benefits of your product over someone else's product. Sometimes marketing materials for channels even name specific competitor's products and describe the features in a way that the differences are readily obvious. The situation may require you to provide such materials.

It is essential to understand the channels' selling model so that you can position your product to get the attention of channel sales representatives. How are they incentivized? Some channels such as distributors create incentives for their sales people that are based on the "discount" on products. Their sales people are trained to sell more of those products that will yield a higher margin for the distributor, because they will get additional commission from them as individuals. If that is the case, you need to understand the terms of your contract with that distributor to find out what the discount will be for your product. Depending on whether that is favorable to you or not, you may need to create ways to get the sales representative's attention.

The second step is to define the limits of the business relationship or contract arrangement between your company and the channel partner. In the agreement, there should be specifications as to discount rate, volume incentives, cooperative marketing funds or arrangements, and term of the agreement (how long it will be in place). Becoming familiar with the specifics of the agreement will help you identify how important or profitable this channel partner might be, which marketing programs can be implemented, and whether this will be a long-term business relationship. Knowing this information will help you prioritize and plan the channel marketing programs or cooperative events that you might want to participate in for the product that you are launching.

The third step is to define what kind of information the channel's sales people need so that they can understand the features, functions and benefits of your product. Almost always, the channel will need marketing materials that are different from those you developed for your company's sales force. Indirect channels usually want very simplified, "quick reference" types of materials. They normally do not need elaborate brochures with graphics and lots of text; they just need the facts about your product and why they should choose to sell it. It is important to remember that they will be selling your product along with your competitors' products. Anything you can do to help organize the information and present it in a simple fashion will increase the chances that they will sell yours.

Indirect channel training

Sometimes, companies develop and implement formal training programs for their channel partners. Such training programs are targeted differently than those for direct channels. If you recall, the sales training information for the direct sales force can contain proprietary or company-internal information, and also information about the competition. You can't include such information when training channels. That means you must create a separate set of training materials for channels that address the features, advantages and customer benefits of your product without revealing your company's internal strategy or what you think of your competition.

Multiple channels

Most companies have more than one distribution channel for their products. This creates a challenge in the areas of managing accounts, making trade-offs between direct and indirect sales based on profitability, and choosing the most effective channels.

How your company deals with these challenges will determine the relative priority that each channel will have at the time of launch. For example, let's assume that your company has decided for account management purposes that the direct sales force will only sell in North America, and that the company will use indirect channels in Europe. You will need to plan to develop one set of materials for the sales force for the North American market, and another set (with possible translations) for the indirect channel.

Sometimes channels do not perform up to expectations or have varying degrees of profitability. In those instances, your company management may decide to place less emphasis on those channels, and the marketing programs for the launch may need to be modified accordingly. It's best to assess this situation early in the launch phase so that the launch plan will contain the right deliverables for the channels.

Launching to channels

Preparing the right marketing materials for all channels can be complicated, as we have seen from the examples in this chapter. In addition, the channels need to receive this information before the announcement date, which creates additional time pressure to develop and deliver the channel marketing materials or programs. The earlier in the launch process that you can assess the channel marketing needs, the easier it will be to work these requirements into the overall launch plan.

Now that you have defined your product, customer, market, competition and channels of distribution, you have enough information to begin the formulation of a marketing strategy. The strategic objectives that were identified will also play a key role in shaping the strategy that will not only meet the business goals for the company, but also the market goals for your product.

PART II

Market Stratgy and Programs

8

Market Strategy

Once you have collected and analyzed all of the data about your product, market, customer, competition, and channels, it is time to synthesize this information and define your market strategy. There is a lot of confusion about what constitutes a "market strategy". Some people think it's a "promotional strategy". For instance, if you ask a businessperson what their market strategy is, they might say, "Oh, we mainly use the web. It's cheaper than print ads." This response describes just one marketing program used by the company to promote the product – the web.

Market strategy is very high-level and encompasses more than just the list of promotional programs you will use when you launch the product. A complete market strategy must describe how you will capture the target market share and maintain competitive advantage, and the timing of market entry. Figure 8.1 illustrates this concept.

Market strategy *IS NOT A:*
- *promotional program*
- *distribution channel*
- *business or operations model*
- *marketing message*
- *differentiator*
- *partner strategy*
- *business objective*

Market strategy *IS A:*

High-level statement that describes how market share will be captured and how competitive advantage will be maintained. Also, if it's a new target market, it includes the timing of market entry.

Figure 8.1 Definition of Market Strategy

An example of a market strategy is the "First-mover Strategy". This describes a situation in which the company intends to be the first to introduce a product to a new market – this describes the timing of market entry (as soon as possible in order to be first). The First-Mover strategy also implies that the company will be recognized as the first to market and will therefore have greater awareness among the customers in that market, leading to a greater market share. Finally, the company's increased recognition and reputation for being the first is how the company will maintain its competitive advantage.

Establishing an effective market strategy for the launch takes some science, some art, and a little intuition. Companies have experimented with various market strategies for decades. A market strategy that works in one industry may not transfer well to another. For example, using the same strategy to sell semiconductor equipment and Internet services would not be effective because the dynamics of the markets are different, as are the sales cycles. There are, however, a few elements of older strategies that can work in today's economy, and some new strategies used today have roots in some of the older strategies. Figure 8.2 shows the old strategies and evolved strategies still in use today.

Market Strategies

-Low price leader   -First-mover + dominate
-Quality leader   -Market segmentation
-Technology leader   -Coopetition
-Differentiation   -One to one marketing
-Branding by itself   -Word-of-mouth
-Merger or acquisition

Figure 8.2 Market Strategies - Old and Evolved

During the days of the industrial economy, some of the most effective market strategies were based on price, cost, or quality differences, and later, technology was a primary differentiator. Other strategies are based on competitors and the market environment, such as differentiation and branding. Companies also used mergers or acquisition as a market strategy. In the 1980s, the first-mover and market domination strategy became popular. Market segmentation was used more often as markets became more fragmented and diverse. Coopetition is a rare strategy involving partnering with competitors for mutual market gain. One to one marketing got its start with the advent of electronic commerce in the 1990s. Word of mouth is actually a very old strategy that was adapted to the online world and was given a new name: affiliate marketing.

Internet technology, email, pressure to get to market faster and increasing competition have created a need for some "hybrid" strategies, as shown in Figure 8.3.

Hybrid Strategies for
Today's Economy

1: Develop and conquer through partnering
    -mutual commitment of resources, common business model and target market

2: Niche differentiation
    -use differentiators to capture target market share but without domination

3: Incremental personalization
    -focus on one customer at a time to build lifetime customer base

4: Growth through referrals
    -proactive referrals, incentives with control

Figure 8.3 Market Strategies Today

These hybrid strategies combine some of the elements of the old strategies with some new twists. These new strategies have been used successfully over the last few years for companies of all sizes.

You may choose to adopt one of these strategies for your launch if there is a fit with your customer, product, and market. The approach to developing a market strategy involves answering these questions:

-Who and where are my customers?

-Will my product meet their need?

-Who else could sell something similar to that customer and how many are there?

Of course, you now have the answers to these questions because you have gathered all of the data and conducted the market and competitive analysis. Now it's a matter of putting it all together to see what strategy makes sense. When you have settled on a strategy, then it's time to develop a detailed description of it. This process is called positioning, which means defining your product's place in the target market in terms of competitors, type of customers, timing of introduction, price, and market share. In order to get the product to the market, it is critical to determine precisely where you are going, when you will go there, and who else will be there. Positioning helps you stake out and describe your territory: your target market.

The process of positioning involves taking the key product differentiators and information about the market and customer and developing positioning statements. The sources of data for market strategy and positioning are shown in Figure 8.4

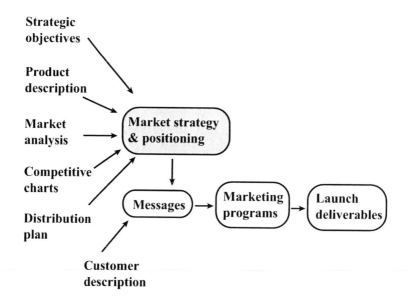

Figure 8.4 Sources of Data for Market Strategy

The earlier chapters of the book, Chapters 2 through 7, outlined the data that needed to be gathered and analyzed in order to assess the product and market. All of the information gathered during that process can and should be used when formulating positioning statements. This includes product definition and product strategy, company strategic objectives, market characteristics, customer definition and buying behavior, competitive analysis and the distribution plan. Information on key differentiators as defined in Chapter 6 must be considered when developing positioning statements. Differentiators capture your key competitive advantage in the marketplace, and therefore your position relative to competitors. Other key information includes the strengths and weaknesses of your company and competitors, also described in Chapter 6. Sometimes, customer stories or feedback from beta testing programs may be available early enough in the product launch phase to use in positioning statements. Such information may give you more clues as to how you need to be positioned in the marketplace. After the market strategy and positioning is complete, the marketing messages need to be developed and the marketing programs need to be identified. The marketing programs then become the launch deliverables.

Positioning statements are an expression of your marketing strategy goals and are meant for company-internal use only. The primary use of these statements is to develop appropriate marketing messages that will communicate your marketing strategy to the external world. The vehicles for communicating the messages are your marketing programs. Implementing marketing programs is how you finally launch your product into the market. Positioning is therefore a very critical step in your launch strategy.

Pricing and its role in positioning

Pricing should be examined while doing competitive analysis at the product-level, so by the time you reach the strategy phase of the launch cycle, you will know how your product will compare to the prices of existing products from your competitors. Sometimes companies place so much emphasis on price differences that their positioning is articulated only in terms of price, such as "We are positioned at the low end of the market." Price is an important factor to consider when determining positioning because price can affect customer perception and therefore demand, as shown in Figure 8.5.

If your product's price is:	Demand will increase if:	Demand will decrease if:
Higher than competitor's	Customer-perceived value > competitor's	Customer-perceived value = competitor's
Same as competitor's	Customer-perceived value > competitor's	Customer-perceived value < competitor's
Lower than competitor's	Customer-perceived value = or > competitor's	Customer-perceived value < competitor's

Figure 8.5 Customer's Perception of Value and Price

Fluctuations in demand, supply, and competitors' pricing strategy complicate the situation. However, if you focus on the customer's value proposition and have some idea of the pricing sensitivity of your target customers, you will be much better prepared to establish a price that will help you get to market and maintain competitive advantage. Usually at the time that launch work begins, the prices are already established for the product to be launched. Sometimes, however, there may be room for flexibility to adjust the price up or down depending on the results of the positioning analysis. If your success in getting to market and reaching revenue goals require that the price be adjusted, then it may be a good idea to revisit the issue before the marketing and launch plans are finalized.

Levels of positioning

Positioning needs to be done at several different levels. The highest level is the company level. Every time that your company launches a new product into the market, you are launching the company as well. If the company image has changed, or if there have been fundamental changes in your company's strategy, a product launch creates an opportunity to reinforce the new changes or image for the company.

The next level of positioning is the product line level, or as it sometimes called, the product strategy level. The product that you are launching is usually part of a larger group of products or is part of a longer-term product strategy. How do you want the market to perceive your product strategy? This is important to define because if you are entering a new market or introducing the first in a series of products, you will need to set the foundation for the products that are launched after yours. In this situation, you may need to provide more information to the market in the initial launch about how your product demonstrates your company's greater technology capabilities and longer-term product strategy.

Finally, the lowest level of positioning that needs to be developed is the product level. This is the most specific and most detailed level of positioning. This level of positioning often involves making price comparisons with competitors' products. Sometimes, price versus performance comparisons are made between your product and competitors' products, and the information is plotted on a graph.

Developing positioning statements

The goal of the positioning process is to develop statements that define your targeted place in the market. These statements describe where your product and company fit relative to other companies and products in the marketplace and may also address when you enter a market. Information used for company-level positioning comes from strategic objectives, the market data and research, and the competitive analysis (particularly the strengths and weaknesses of your company and competitors). Sometimes the middle level of positioning is called the solution level, especially if the product being launched is software. Quite often, software packages or tools are complementary to other software or are designed to be part of a broader customer solution. In that case, positioning needs to be done that describes what your product contributes to the overall solution. Information needed for product line or solution positioning comes from the product definition, the differentiators that were identified during competitive analysis, and the customer benefits. Compiling a price-performance graph is a good way to visually display the product-level positioning. The information compiled during the competitive analysis, such as the competitive matrix, the differentiators and the FAB chart, are the main sources for development of product-level positioning. Strategic objectives also can affect your product level positioning.

All positioning statements are relative to something else or someone else or to a unit in time or a quantitative measure. Here are some examples of positioning statements, along with the designated level:

The XY4000 server will be the first high-end solution available at a price that small businesses can afford. We will be the first company to offer this combination of price and performance to the small office-home office market. (company level)

The goal of SizzleCo is to enter the financial services market with our real-time alert software. (company level)

Although our XLNT productivity tools are priced higher than IBM's test suite, they offer more reporting capabilities for QA managers. The QA managers get more value for the money. (product level)

With the new WD40 design software, we can outperform AgileCAD, and maintain our majority market share. (company level)

ConnecTool can be used to report link errors in any type of web design software, regardless of operating system. It can be used to enhance the performance of any suite of website development packages. (solution level)

The examples above subtly reveal strengths and weaknesses of the company or product, such as higher price (example 3) or challenges to market share (example 4). It is entirely appropriate to capture the weaknesses of the product or company in positioning statements, because it will help in formulating a strategy to overcome the weaknesses. Example 3 above contains a reference to customer-perceived value as a means of overcoming the higher product price. Any marketing material for the product in Example 3 should emphasize customer-perceived value instead of price. In Example 4, the company expresses hope to maintain its market share through better product-level performance. Similarly, any marketing material should emphasize higher performance of the product. Sometimes, the very act of writing positioning statements will result in ideas for presenting the product to the market in a more favorable light.

Positioning statements need to capture where you are going in the market relative to competitors. As long as the statements clearly convey the strategy that will maximize your competitive advantage, they will be sufficient. The objectives are quality and completeness, not quantity.

Special cases

Channel positioning may also need to be done. This is especially true if your company is using a new distribution channel. Your company must establish itself within the channel's selling infrastructure, along with positioning relative to your competitors. A sample positioning statement for a channel might be:

> *We want IBM to start integrating our network security software into their European customer base. Ours is the only package on the market that meets European standards.*

In this example, the goal is to establish your product in the channel first by convincing the channel sales representatives that the product is superior.

The process of positioning can and should be used for specific marketing events such as trade shows. These events represent venues in which you may have exposure to a portion of your target market. Study the demographics of the trade show; are potential customers likely to attend? If so, how can you plan for your company, product line and product to be represented at the trade show? One positioning statement might be:

> *At the Network World show, our booth is across the aisle from our main competitor. We need to demo our new software package in our booth to show that it's much faster than the other guy's product.*

This is a product-level positioning statement for that event. It may not be the only product-level positioning statement, but it might be the best opportunity to highlight that particular differentiator.

Positioning may become more complicated in international markets. Sometimes there may be different competitors in each country, and positioning may need to be done on a country-by-country basis. International markets may also involve greater reliance on channels, and in those instances channel positioning may also need to be done.

When you have completed the development of your positioning statements, you will be ready to begin crafting the messages that will be carried through to your customer through marketing materials and programs.

9

Message Development and Usage

The positioning statements that were developed in the last chapter are meant for company-internal use. Before those statements can be used to help implement your market strategy, they need to be translated into a form that is suitable for external use. This translation process is called messaging.

During the messaging process, you identify the information that is to be communicated to the market and the means by which this information will be communicated. In order to make sure that the messages will resonate with the target customer, the customer characterization is another major source of information that is used during the process. The output of this process is a list of messages that can be used in marketing materials. Positioning represents your product strategy; messages implement that strategy through communications.

Figure 9.1 shows the source material that is used to compile messages.

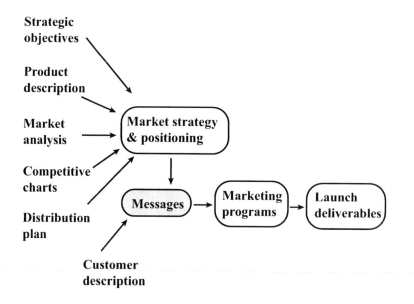

Figure 9.1 Source Material for Messages

The process of messaging is often done by a marketing communications group, sometimes referred to as "MarCom". Some companies may instead use an internal corporate communications group, that is typically more focused on public relations than marketing but that has similar skills. The art of developing effective marketing messages is closely tied to communications theory. The objective is to get the attention of the listener or the reader, and then to communicate the information that ultimately will result in some action being taken by the receiver of the message. In this case, the desired action is for the receiver of the message to buy your product.

The result of the messaging process is a hierarchy of marketing messages that is used primarily as an outline for the marketing materials and programs that will be developed during the launch. The professionals who develop marketing materials use this list as a guide when writing copy, designing graphics or multimedia presentations, and developing marketing events such as seminars or road shows. Messages also provide a framework and checklist for the marketing strategy throughout the launch phase. Once they have been developed, messages usually are compiled into a section in the marketing plan that is used to guide the launch. Here are some examples of marketing messages:

Our GO480 system will give you the performance you need for your e-commerce infrastructure, along with the flexibility to add up to 4 more servers for minimal additional investment.

Our OpenNet software enables a single-system view from any desktop, for ease of administration.

Connect to your ISP anywhere, any time with the RovNet wireless adapter. Keeping you mobile is our number one concern.

PowerNET is rated number one in customer satisfaction. Because we build our products with your networking needs in mind, you receive custom solutions for an off-the-shelf price.

You may notice that these messages sound very different than the positioning statements. Positioning statements reveal strategic intentions, but in the messages, the strategy is "hidden". Messages contain information about product features, functions, and customer benefits, and they are formulated to meet strategic objectives and implement product positioning.

How many messages are needed?

Messages are used to communicate information about the product being launched in an effort to convince the customer to buy the product. Figure 9.2 shows the customer buying cycle and its various stages.

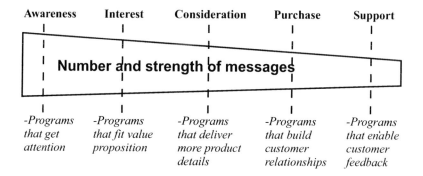

Awareness   Interest   Consideration   Purchase   Support

Number and strength of messages

-Programs
that get
attention

-Programs
that fit value
proposition

-Programs
that deliver
more product
details

-Programs
that build
customer
relationships

-Programs
that enable
customer
feedback

Figure 9.2 Customer Buying Cycle and Number of
Messages Needed

The launch phase covers the first three stages leading up to Purchase: the Awareness, Interest, and Consideration stages. Moving from left to right, it is during these three stages that the greatest number of messages will be needed to effect a product purchase. Some of these messages will be high-level and strategic; others will be more specific and relate directly to the customer problem. It is best to develop a hierarchy of messages that cover the company-level and product-level messages. How many do you need? You'll definitely need more than one, because you can't write a piece of marketing collateral with one message repeated in every paragraph. Err on the side of too many; you don't have to use them all. Ten key messages should be a minimum number to start with. You'll need some messages in each category: those that relate to your customer's problem, those that describe your product/service, and those that differentiate you from the competition.

Crafting messages

Developing effective messaging is a tricky proposition. Messages are difficult to nail down, challenging to express, and absolutely essential for reaching your customer. Everyone has his or her own idea of the key messages that should be used in a launch. Senior level managers usually want succinct, distilled messages that reflect one or more high-level corporate strategies or competitive advantages. Product managers will most often focus on the product features and functions. And somewhere in between, there is a compromise that will result in the right messages for your target customer.

During the process of developing messages, you need to accomplish the following:

-Identify the key factors that differentiate your company/product from your competition
-Characterize the key product features and functions
-Describe how the product or service solves a business problem for the customer, i.e., benefits
-Incorporate the strategic objectives of the company
-Implement your positioning

The process of crafting messages includes gathering all of the essential information you need for developing message content, formulating messages, getting them reviewed and prioritized, and, finally, compiling them into a message hierarchy.

Content of messages

The process of developing messages includes gathering the source material, identifying key words and phrases, formulating the messages, and compiling a hierarchy. The information you developed when you analyzed your customer and the market, the FAB charts, your positioning statements, and the identified strategic objectives are all sources of content for messages. If the timing works out, you may also have customer quotes from a beta testing program or other types of "live" customer feedback. This information should also be considered as source content for messages.

The first step in developing message content is to make a list of the primary customer needs met by your product that have value for your customer. The basic objectives of your messages are to create awareness and to get customers to buy your product. In order to accomplish this, you need to know enough about the buying behavior of your customers to understand how to get their attention. When you did your customer analysis, you identified the customer's needs and value propositions. It's a good idea to list those customer needs and value propositions when developing the messages, because this information is the most important content for messages. It's how you get potential customers to recognize a need they have and gain an awareness that your product fulfills that need.

The next step is to revisit the FAB chart and list the differentiators for your product. Differentiators are expressed in relative terms, such as:
> -Faster
> -Higher quality
> -More open
> -Multiplatform, multisystem, vendor independent
> -Global, worldwide, international

When you construct the list, be sure to include the company-level differentiators as well as the product-level differentiators from the FAB chart. The last step is to list the positioning statements and the strategic objectives that you have identified for your product.

Gather together your list of customer needs and differentiators, the strategic objectives and positioning statements. Using that material as a reference, start by thinking about which WORDS should be used to:

-convey the value of your product/service
-differentiate your product/company from that of your competitors
-show that you understand the customer's problem or situation
-educate the customer about what the product is and does

Begin by listing out key WORDS that relate to the situation – just brainstorm, which means anything goes. Words that convey value or demonstrate differentiation might be: faster, higher, stronger, effective, high-quality, superior, world-class, right, any, low-cost. Words and phrases that show you understand your customer's problem might include things like: "in today's dynamic economy", "maximizing your IT investment", or "freeing up resources to be used more effectively". These phrases should relate to a business problem that your customer has. The words and phrases (and sometimes numbers) that educate your customer about the product should be factual, descriptive, and truthful; don't exaggerate. Examples are:

-Our anti-virus program is integrated with the main application
-We offer a range of services suitable for organizations up to 500 people
-Our smart card technology is consistent with European standards

After this exercise, you will have a list of words and phrases to build a hierarchy of messages. The following example will show the whole sequence of steps.

Let's assume that your product is a broadband router for multimedia applications and design collaboration. Your product solution provides interoperability across disparate networks, with broadband speeds, and was designed to handle large graphics or design files. Your nearest competitor has a similar solution, but it only handles small graphics files and doesn't support collaboration. That same competitor has a poor reputation for support services to integrate and install their products.

From this example, your customer needs are:
-Interoperability at broadband speeds
-Collaboration support
-Multimedia application support

Your differentiators are:
-Collaborative design support
-Unlimited multimedia file support
-Better system integration services

Your strategic objective is to leverage your system integrator partners more, in order to enter the enterprise market. Your positioning statement was:

The new DM2000 system will be used as our first opportunity to enter the enterprise market, where BBG Systems dominates the market. We will have to emphasize our SI support in order to enter this market.

Here are the messages that can be crafted from the content:

1) We offer complete solutions for routing multimedia broadband communications, including collaborative design support.
2) With our experienced integration partners, we can quickly implement a broadband solution for your short-term needs, and support enhancements of your infrastructure as your needs evolve.
3) The DM2000 router can handle any size of media file at broadband speeds.

In the messaging process, the trick is to distill the content into key words and phrases, and then recombine them into message statements. You can repeat key words and phrases for emphasis.

Structure and style of messages

As we have seen so far from the examples in this chapter, the structure of messages can vary. Messages can be worded to convey a relative comparison (more powerful, complete solution), a claim (easier to use, greater flexibility), or a statement of fact (rated number one, broadband speeds).

The style of messages may be dictated by corporate guidelines, either formal or informal. External marketing literature and public relations material may need to be consistent with a corporate "look and feel", in order to reinforce the company image or reputation. This will need to be taken into account when developing messages.

Messages can be very subtle, almost "subliminal", or bold, direct claims. Sometimes, messages can be too overpowering or can contain buzzwords or flowery phrases that serve to irritate people rather than to inform them. These buzzwords and phrases are sometimes referred to as "marketing fluff" or "marketspeak". The messaging process is a time for creativity, but not at the expense of turning off your listener or reader. Beware of overused terms and catchy phrases. The best way to test the wording of messages is to have people from a variety of disciplines in your company review the messages, before you start using them in externally-targeted materials.

Messages can be conveyed in words, pictures, and sound. Text, or the written word, is by far the most common form of messages. However, the variety of multimedia tools and communications channels available today offers many new ways to convey marketing messages. Photos, illustrations, or videos that help viewers to identify with the situation in which your product may be used are a very powerful way to convey a message. Photos enable the viewers to imagine themselves in that same situation and may move them one step closer to buying your product. Messages in audio form, such as cassettes, CDs, or radio broadcasts, can often have similar effects.

Telling the marketing story

Now that you have a whole pile of messages ready to go, it's time to put them together into effective marketing copy. It means taking the words and phrases, forming sentences and paragraphs to create a marketing "story". For anyone who has ever taken a writing class, the first thing you learn is that a story has a beginning, middle and an end. The only difference between a story and marketing material is that rather than entertain the reader, the marketing material is supposed to inform the reader – although there is no reason why marketing copy can't be entertaining as well. Don't be afraid to take a unique approach or have fun with it, within reason.

Suppose that the marketing piece is a brochure that has some text and some graphics. The beginning of the marketing "story" should immediately get the reader's (customer's) attention. At the very beginning, use the messages that relate to your customer's problem. The reader/customer must relate to the marketing copy right away or they won't continue reading. In the middle section, use the factual content about your product and service and how it solves the problem. The end should contain the messages about your key differentiators, with a final statement that relates back to your customer's problem again. You've come full circle with your marketing story now. You've told your customer you understand their problem, that you have a solution, that your solution is unique and will have value for them. If you have a brochure with about 6 paragraphs of total copy, the first will be the customer problem paragraph, the next 3 should be about your product/service, the next one should be about your differentiators, and the last paragraph should include a repeat of the customer problem and a wrap-up summary sentence. The graphics in the brochure can help to illustrate the messages from the beginning, middle or end sections.

Using the message hierarchy as an outline

A list of messages can be used as an outline for creating drafts of marketing collateral. By listing the messages, the writer or designer of the piece can arrange the points that need to be made in the document and then expand upon the messages by adding words and illustrations. If the messages are ranked in terms of priority, then the most important messages may need to be used several times or in several places in the document in order to reinforce the point. Sometimes variations of the key messages are also used in a "side-bar" piece in a document, often in a bulleted list. This is another way to emphasize key messages. Other types of marketing materials such as presentations can also be developed by using a list of messages. The format of a presentation lends itself to bulleted lists of key points. Key messages can be reworded or illustrations can be created to emphasize these points.

Using messages in marketing materials

Using messages in marketing materials is a matter of understanding how the content is laid out. With printed material such as brochures, white papers and datasheets, there are many places within the material to add text and tell the marketing story with the messages. Multimedia programs such as CDs and video represent opportunities to convey messages visually. Multimedia gives you an opportunity to show your customer the benefits of your product and not just tell your customer about the product. The worldwide web not only has multimedia capabilities for conveying your messages, but it also can be interactive. This adds another dimension to messaging, enabling a greater level of detail for messages. Interactive websites can convey all of the messages contained in your written marketing materials as well as your multimedia materials, but you can add additional levels of messaging if the potential customer wants more information. Interactive questions and answers, production selection guides and other such tools allow more opportunities to convey messages at any level of detail. Figure 9.3 is a diagram showing the possible venues for messages:

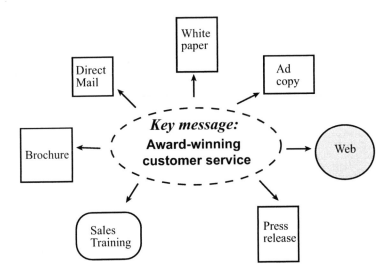

*Figure 9.3 **How and Where to Use Messages***

In the above example, your company has just received an award for customer service among your industry peers. How would this message be used in the various marketing materials? Starting at the top of the diagram, the first item is a white paper. A white paper usually consists of three parts: an industry or technology trend, impact on the customer, and how your company addresses this issue with your product or service. For this message, you could add customer service as a trend in the first part of the white paper, and then in the third part explain how your customer delivers superior service. Moving clockwise, the next item is advertising copy. This is easy to incorporate your message of superior customer service; you could have a photo of the award and incorporate it into the ad. You could also state the same in text: "We are the winners of this year's award for outstanding customer service." The next category is the company website. On the homepage, you should have an image of the award with an animated caption such as: "Voted #1 in customer service in our industry". You could also add this small slogan to other pages of the website to reinforce that message.

Regarding the press release, you could write an entire release about the fact that your company won the award because that constitutes industry news. Adding a customer quote that attests to your superior level of service would also help reinforce the message. In sales training, the leader or instructor could tell the salespeople to mention this award during their sales calls, as a way of reminding customers about the importance of customer service to the company. A brochure could carry this message as a tagline near the end of the brochure near the company contact information; you could also have a small paragraph about the commitment to customer service. The last item is the direct mail or email piece, which would be very similar to the press release, except it can be more personalized for the recipient.

Regardless of the means you use to communicate your messages, consistency is extremely important. There is nothing worse than having to explain why two different pieces of marketing literature make conflicting claims about the product. Make sure that everyone involved in developing marketing materials has the "master" set of messages and understands their meaning.

Compiling the messaging plan

Once you have determined the list of messages you will use and the media or vehicles you will use to communicate the messages, this information should be documented in a messaging plan, or communications plan. This plan should specify all of the messages that need to be conveyed, and how the messages will be used in the various venues or marketing programs including written collateral, multimedia formats, and the web. This plan should then be reviewed and approved by the appropriate management representatives before it is implemented. When this messaging plan has been approved, it becomes a section in the marketing plan, so that it can serve as a reference throughout the launch.

Keeping messages current

Product launches don't always go smoothly. Products evolve, market conditions change, and corporations sometimes change direction during the launch phase. These changes can affect your marketing messages and also their relative priority. When significant changes occur, address them immediately and re-visit the messages. If you change the messages, be sure to maintain consistency in all of the marketing materials to eliminate confusion in the external market.

At the end of the message development process, you will have a messaging plan that will form the basic reference to be used through the rest of the launch planning process. You will refer to the messaging plan when you develop marketing programs, write the marketing plan, and implement the launch plan.

10

External Marketing Programs

By this time, you have gathered a substantial amount of information about your customer, the market, your strategy, and your messages. It is now time to develop the vehicles that will carry your messages into the market. This is the first step in preparing the market for your product. The communication vehicles and materials developed during the launch process that are used to prepare the marketplace are referred to as marketing programs. Marketing programs directed at customers and the outside world are called external marketing programs. Marketing programs focused on educating your sales force, employees, and sometimes your channel partners, are called internal marketing programs and are discussed in detail in Chapter 12.

External marketing programs consist of the information and events that you use to educate your customers and convince them to buy your products. These programs are often called deliverables, because they are the output of the launch process that will be delivered to the market. Materials that sales representatives give to customers to help sell products are often referred to by a special name: collateral. In this book, we will use this term in a broad sense to refer to any materials that are given to customers. We will refer to printed material as print collateral and electronic material, such as web content and email as electronic collateral. External marketing programs, then, include collateral (both print and electronic), advertising and public relations activities, events such as tradeshows and seminars, and miscellaneous programs including demos, presentations, multimedia, sales training and sales guides, and information placed on product packages. In short, any marketing information that can be seen, heard, or touched by a customer prospect is included in the definition of external marketing programs.

Choosing external marketing programs

With such a wide variety of formats to choose from, how do you determine the best external marketing programs to use? This decision is driven by several factors, including budget, availability of resources, company policies, type of customer and market, strategic objectives, and positioning.

The marketing budget is a major factor in deciding the types and the size of external marketing programs. Budgets are determined well in advance of a launch, sometimes several months or even a year before. Sometimes when a product is launched you develop unique external marketing programs that you'd like to implement, but that are not covered in the budget. In that situation, trade-offs must be made in order to stay within budget guidelines, or a proposal to obtain more funding must be submitted to management. The cost of each deliverable must be weighed against the customer impact, as shown on Figure 10.1.

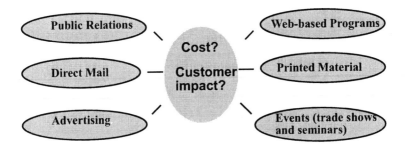

The cost of the program needs to balance with the impact the program will have on the customer

Figure 10.1 Program Cost and Customer Impact

Each program will have a specific cost, ranging from a few hundred dollars to several thousand dollars. Sometimes programs that cost a lot will have little impact, and sometimes those that cost very little can have a huge impact on the customer and result in sales. Each program needs to be evaluated in terms of return on investment. It's advisable to have a 'balanced' program portfolio, with a mix of programs that will be most effective for the target audience.

Resource availability is another factor that impacts your choice of marketing programs. Sometimes, the marketing professionals in your company who are responsible for doing specific types of programs are fully utilized on other projects and don't have time to work on your launch. If that is the case, you must decide whether to bring in outside help, or to do only the external marketing programs that can be implemented by available staff.

Sometimes, companies have policies that determine the types of external marketing programs that they will or won't pursue. These policies may be driven by strategic objectives or budget considerations. Examples of such policies are:

Beginning with the 3rd quarter of this year, we will no longer do product-level advertising.

Brochures will no longer be distributed at trade shows. We will provide the content on our website instead.

Policies such as these may have been implemented after evaluating the effectiveness of external marketing programs in previous launches. The examples above suggest that for that particular company, product-level advertising and brochures had not been successful in terms of bringing in more revenue for the products, compared to the cost of these programs. Sometimes companies also implement policies that relate to corporate image campaigns and the need to focus media attention on the company rather than at the product level. You need to be aware of these corporate-level directives and policies before you determine which external marketing programs will be pursued during the launch implementation phase.

The customer environment and market segment characteristics also affect your choice of external marketing programs. Customer buying behavior may dictate the forms of marketing materials that will be most successful. Suppose, for example, that your target customers never go to trade shows, never read their mail (except email), and spend more than half of their average workday on the web. This narrows your choices for reaching those customers; you'd better put the marketing material on your website. Certain vertical market segments have specific events where everybody who is anybody in that industry attends, in order to update their knowledge and to mingle.

If that is the case, then you may need to have some presence at that event to increase your product's visibility.

Strategic objectives and positioning statements are also key factors in determining external marketing programs. Suppose that a key strategic objective is to enter a new market segment where there is one major competitor. A positioning statement that might follow from this strategic objective is:

We will focus on our multimedia capabilities in order to beat NetPro in the manufacturing market; they only have basic data functionality.

Because your company and products are new to the market in this situation, you will need programs that build awareness of your product, such as advertising, press tours and public events. You will also need external marketing programs that support every possible way of reaching your new customer, including product demonstrations. And, in this case, they should be multimedia product demonstrations.

Who chooses the external marketing programs? Companies vary considerably in the area of marketing program decisions, mainly because marketing organizations are organized differently in every company. In most cases, the product marketing organization needs to work together with the marketing communications organization, if indeed they are separate. Sometimes there is only one marketing organization in a company, and sometimes there is just one individual. The best way to make decisions about the number and types of external marketing programs is to obtain input from all of the organizations that have a key role in the product launch process, or the organizational representatives who may serve on the launch team.

The choice of external marketing programs needs to be determined very early in the launch process, before the launch plan is developed. The recommended marketing programs and their details need to be documented in the marketing plan, which is then implemented during the remainder of the launch process.

Sometimes, it is necessary to reprioritize the external marketing programs during the launch if market conditions or strategic objectives change. If a prioritized list of these programs is captured in the marketing plan, it is easier to make revisions, should the need arise.

Recommended programs for major and routine launches

For a startup company or established company that is launching a brand new product, more external marketing programs will be required in order to build awareness of the company as well as the new product. At other times a company will be launching another in a series of products, so fewer programs are needed. And some companies develop a standard set of external marketing programs that are done for every launch on a routine basis. Figure 10.2 is a checklist of programs for major or routine launches.

Company launch/ new product launch	Routine product launch or enhancement
-Press release, press/ analyst tour -Brochure -Datasheet -White paper -Demo, if appropriate -Selected advertising -Big website splash -Events (trade shows, user conferences) -Sales training materials, collateral kit -Sales tools -Channel programs	-Press releases -Datasheet -White paper -Demo, if appropriate -Website update -Sales training materials -Customer presentation -Events (depending on timing -Channel program update

Figure 10.2 Marketing Programs for Major and Routine Launches

Often, there will be formalized templates or guidelines in place for creating these materials and programs, to avoid reinventing the wheel each time. Implementing a standard set of programs is much faster than coming up with entirely new programs. If there is a set of standard programs already in place, and if they continue to be effective programs for the marketplace, then they should be implemented during the new launch. Using standard external marketing programs has pros and cons. The pros include speed of execution, lower cost, and consistency of information for the marketplace. The cons include staleness of formats, lack of innovation that negatively affects the company's image, and difficulty in distinguishing one product from another.

Standard marketing programs can be livened up by adding a new format or a new vehicle for delivering the content, such as the web or a CD. Defining new programs and integrating them with standard ones also helps create more of an interesting "portfolio" of programs.

Types of external marketing programs

The remainder of this chapter describes the different types of external marketing programs and gives guidelines on when and how to use them. The following categories of external marketing programs are discussed in this chapter: print collateral, electronic collateral, events, and miscellaneous programs. Advertising and public relations campaigns constitute a major topic, and are discussed in detail in Chapter 11.

Print collateral

Print collateral has been used for decades as the primary tool for educating sales people and customers about new products. In high tech industries, the datasheet has been a staple of the collateral collection; if nothing else was created, the datasheet was used for everything. Print collateral now generally includes datasheets, white papers, brochures and to some extent, direct mail pieces. Sometimes, print collateral is used as content for multimedia programs or as a supplement to the information presented at live events.

Datasheets
A datasheet is a concise document, usually two to four pages in length, that gives the following key elements for a product: a description, functionality and key features, applications, benefits, technical specifications, a picture or schematic (optional), and company contact information. In the world of high tech

marketing, datasheets are a basic requirement. Technical people use datasheets more than any other type of collateral; they want to check the technical specifications of the product, and they expect to see either photos of the product or diagrams that illustrate how the product works. In terms of style and tone, a datasheet needs to be concise, technical and not flashy. Sometimes the front and back of a single sheet are used.

White papers
Originally developed and named in the military world, white papers were written by scientists, researchers, and government contractors to obtain research and development funding. In today's world of high tech marketing, white papers are basically technical documents that also contain marketing messages. Usually six to twelve pages in length, the content of a white paper is meant to inform and educate the reader about technology and / or business trends, and thus, the style of writing is educational. A white paper usually contains several elements: a description of a major new technology trend or phenomenon, a discussion of a technology solution that either contributes to the trend or solves a problem created by the trend, and a sales pitch: how your product solves the problem or furthers the positive trends.

White papers are used for many purposes. They can be used as sales collateral, as trade show giveaways, in direct mail, or as website content. If white papers are posted to a company's website they are usually in PDF format for faster downloading. Sometimes, companies will require the site visitor to fill in a form with contact information before the user can download the white paper. White papers have more substantial content than datasheets, and they are more informative and interesting than a brochure.

Brochures

Brochures can be simple, short black-and-white pieces or elaborate productions with lots of artwork and color. They are usually designed in a coordinated fashion so that the graphics or illustrations and the text together convey a specific look and feel. The content of a brochure is usually at a very general level. A brochure doesn't have the technical detail of a datasheet, and it doesn't have a story line like a white paper. Brochures are sales-oriented and contain high level messages aimed at high-level product benefits. Because they are usually expensive to create and reproduce, brochures need to last more than a few months. That is why the content is kept very general and is not technical; otherwise the information would become outdated too quickly. Brochures are generally not distributed widely due to their cost; often they are mailed only to qualified sales leads or to the most promising customer prospects. Sometimes brochures are developed as additional sales collateral if other types of collateral haven't been effective, or if your strategy involves entering a new market where you need to build awareness. Sometimes brochures are developed when there is a change in corporate image or branding; new brochures are created to convey the new image in the marketplace. Because the content of a brochure is at a high level, a brochure is an excellent vehicle for communicating corporate level and solution level messages, but not for communicating product level detail.

Direct mail/email

Direct mail still refers to the old-fashioned way of mailing things to people: via the U.S. Postal service. Today, email is more commonly used, but direct mail is sometimes used to supplement the marketing campaign. Selling targeted mailing lists is still a big business. Traditionally, the "hit rate" of high tech product sales resulting from direct mail is pretty low, and the same applies to email campaigns (especially because everyone is inundated with legitimate email and spam these days). In most instances, direct mail should be used either as a follow-up or as a supplement to other marketing programs. Some exceptions are:

-Sending invitations for special events
-Questionnaires and surveys to do market research
-Pre-announcing trade show booth events
-Newsletters and other material sent regularly to "installed base" customers

Electronic collateral

With the growth of electronic communications, there are more new ways to market new products than ever before. Electronic collateral is becoming the most common way to deliver marketing and sales information to the market. Electronic collateral includes information that is delivered via the worldwide web and corporate intranets.

Web content

The universal adoption of the worldwide web for business purposes has given us many new marketing tools. Corporate websites provides a vehicle for marketing information that can be updated quickly and easily. Marketing material and advertising on the web can reach millions of users worldwide, instantaneously. Companies now rely on the web as a forum for announcing and showcasing new products, along with existing products. Because it is so easy to add material to websites, companies have a tendency to err on the side of excess. Websites can quickly become sluggish and clogged with too much information, and sometimes material isn't organized in a user-friendly fashion. It's critical to keep websites up to date by adding fresh content, and to keep the overall design simple and concise so that site visitors stay long enough to read the content.

For every piece of print collateral developed for the launch, a version of it should be placed on the web. Because company websites are used widely by customers to obtain product information, using the corporate website is a lower cost way to reach more potential customers than by printing collateral. In addition to merely duplicating the print collateral, the web can also be used for interactive tools such as product selection tools, surveys, product demonstrations, and presentations. Video and sound is easily added to websites.

Intranet content

Like the web, corporate intranets are becoming popular as a way to quickly update employees and business partners on critical product information and sales strategies. Although the intranet is the primary vehicle used today for internal marketing, it is discussed in this chapter because it is often used to provide information to business and channel partners external to the company. Companies can easily set up password-controlled access to the intranet for their key strategic partners. Pre-launch product information as well as sales tools and strategic objectives can be distributed via the intranet. Sales training and channel training can be delivered via the corporate intranet as well. Information such as positioning statements and product roadmaps and strategy might also be placed on the intranet. Draft versions of the external marketing materials such as press releases, datasheets, and white papers are often placed on the intranet with controlled access in order to obtain review and comment as the documents are being developed. In summary, any information that your employees, sales staff, and channel partners need to know about your marketing plans and strategy can be placed on the corporate intranet.

Events

Marketing events are those programs where marketing material is presented live and in person. Events include conferences, or tradeshows and seminars. These events usually involve both the marketing and sales organizations to plan, manage and staff the events.

Trade shows and giveaways

At the beginning of the launch process, it is critical to identify the trade shows that your company will be participating in before, during, and after the launch date. Before spending a lot of time and money on demos and marketing materials for your company's booth, develop a high-level strategy and plan for the show. It is extremely important to evaluate the expected demographics of the trade show attendees. If possible, attend other trade shows that serve similar audiences and observe how exhibitors and attendees interact. Which booths have the most traffic and attract the most attendees? How are the most popular booths set up? What types of booth materials are attendees carrying around? This is a great way to obtain specific information before you plan for a trade show.

Designing and implementing trade show booths and giveaways are a whole industry. If you have an internal trade show coordinator, you should meet with him or her about the amount of company booth space that will be available at the show. Live demos or videos at booths may be possible, along with targeted collateral for the specific trade show. Make sure to order the right furniture and electrical connections for your booth to fit the planned activities. Booth signage and displays are becoming more important in booth design, especially with the portable pop-up booths that provide a literal canvas for your company and product information. It's tempting to fill up the entire surface of the display wall with graphics and text, but remember that with people standing in front of it, attendees will only be able to see the top third of the display wall. If you are designing new booth materials for a specific show, you will need to allow enough budget and lead time to design and produce these materials. Sometimes, press releases are planned for release during a trade show to capitalize on the presence of trade press all in one place, and small press conferences can also be held in conjunction with a trade show. If you plan to give away imprinted merchandise at your booth, make sure it's appropriate for the audience and that you allow enough lead time to get the merchandise produced and shipped to the event.

Preparing marketing materials for trade shows can be very complicated. There are two schools of thought about printed materials. Some companies give out copies of datasheets or brochures to everyone who passes by the booth; others only give copies out to interested attendees or sales prospects. Both approaches can be effective, so the choice may depend upon your marketing budget and how many copies you want to print.

Seminars

There are two basic types of seminars: customer seminars, which have a combined educational and marketing focus, and executive seminars. Customer seminars are marketing events that take the form of an educational presentation with a marketing flavor - almost like an "infomercial". These events are either publicized in advance through localized advertising, or they are set up on an invitation-only basis. Often, sales representatives are on hand to answer questions, circulate during breaks and/or a meal, and land new customer accounts. These events can help to build local awareness in a new market, but the downside is that you need to repeat the events in several major cities or regions in order for them to be effective.

Executive seminars are special, invitation-only events where a notable or famous guest speaker gives a talk on a subject of general business interest. The executives from your company then have an opportunity to network and build relationships with the invited external executives. The sponsoring company usually pays expenses for travel and speakers' fees, so these events can be rather expensive. These types of events are normally done when there is a company image rebuilding campaign, or when a company is trying to establish itself in a new industry.

Miscellaneous marketing programs

There are other types of programs that don't conveniently fit in one of the above-mentioned categories that are important and very common parts of product launch. These programs include development of press or sales presentations, product demonstrations, multimedia programs, sales training tools, and product packaging.

Presentations

Slide or viewgraph presentations have become more important in marketing campaigns. They are used to inform the press and customers and to train sales people and channel partners. Presentations are no longer used just for live events. Because presentations are created in electronic form, they can easily be transferred to CD or the web. The presenter can add the audio/video forms of the presentations, and in effect can replicate the live event.

Product demos

If one picture is worth a thousand words about a product, then a demo is worth about ten thousand words. If your product is in a form that lends itself to a demo that can be viewed on a computer monitor or can be videotaped, the demo can be used as a powerful selling tool. Videotaped product demos can be costly and time-consuming to develop and produce. However, the produced demo can then be used in place of live demos done by a person, which may reduce travel costs. Furthermore, translating the demo to a CD or DVD format can greatly increase the number of customer prospects who will see it, and it can be easily mailed, given to customers, or handed out at trade shows.

Multimedia: CD, video, TV and radio

As technology advances, the use of multimedia for marketing campaigns is becoming standard. Laptop and desktop systems, along with the web, enable multimedia marketing. CDs are probably the most common form of media used in marketing campaigns and for the sales force. Because of their portability, they can be used in face-to-face sales situations or can be given to customers as a "leave-behind". Videos are still sometimes used for product demonstrations or more ambitious product presentations. They can range from infomercials to flashy advertising commercials to videotaped technical presentations. Video content can also be replicated on CD and the web. TV and radio are used mainly for advertising campaigns; this is covered in detail in Chapter 11.

Sales training tools

Depending on the size of the sales force, there may be several different types of sales training materials that may need to be developed for the new product. These materials might include product reference or configuration guides, pricing guides, selling ideas and guidelines, or multimedia items such as product selection tools or automated pricing and configuration tools.

There may be a standard set of sales materials that are created for every new product that is launched. It's a good idea to contact the coordinator for sales training to find out what the sales force might require.

Product packaging

Layout, labeling, and product information that are placed on your product's package also need to be addressed as a marketing program during the marketing strategy phase. The positioning and messaging for your product need to extend to the package itself. This is especially true if your product will be sold to consumers or sold through retail channels. Your product must be noticeable if it is sitting on a shelf alongside your competitors' products, or pictured in a mail order catalog. Your product's package must communicate your product differentiators through the package labeling, layout, and information that are on the package. If your product is a new entrant to the market, it may be necessary for the product to appear similar to your competitors' products in order to develop initial awareness. However, it is important to avoid potential trademark infringement by using labeling or layouts that are too similar to your competitors' products. Product packaging is also an effective avenue for communicating and reinforcing corporate-level messages, such as using graphics that convey the company's image, brand, or logo.

Process for defining and prioritizing

You will likely have several different types of external marketing programs that will be implemented during your launch. You should make a list of those that might be appropriate for your situation. Consult with the launch team to identify those that will be effective and consistent with your positioning and your strategy. Rank the programs by categories, depending on whether a program is critical for positioning or merely a "nice to do". Once you have the master list, then evaluate the budget and do another prioritization. Quite often, your budget may result in programs being eliminated from the list.

At this point, you will have a deliverables list of the programs that are most critical and that fit within the launch budget. The next task is to assign owners, who will be responsible for leading those programs during the launch. The output from this exercise will then be used when the launch plan is put together, which is addressed in Chapters 14 and 16.

11

PR and Advertising

Although public relations and advertising are considered external marketing programs, they are so important to the success of product launches that they require discussion in a separate chapter. Public relations campaigns and advertising are central to promoting your new product to the external world. During a public relations campaign, the objective is to develop awareness of your product among the press and analysts, so that they in turn will in turn get the information to your ultimate customer via publications, newspapers, or through other media. This is sometimes referred as getting "ink". In contrast, the objective of advertising is to develop awareness directly with potential customers, with no "intermediary" involved. A public relations campaign may include the issuance of press releases and announcements, press tours with editors and columnists of trade publications, press kits, industry analyst programs, and special events such as seminars and press conferences. Advertising may be accomplished via print, electronic, or broadcast media, as well as through sponsorships. You will likely have a mix of several different types of public relations and advertising programs during your product launch. Timing of public relations campaigns and advertising relative to your launch date is critical because such programs are quite expensive, and careful planning is necessary.

Public relations campaigns

Companies vary greatly in their handling of public relations and corporate communications. Sometimes companies have their own public relations department that handles everything, and sometimes they depend on an outside agency, providing a company liaison to work with the agency. If your company does not have a public relations department, an experienced public relations firm can do wonders for positioning your products and your company in the trade press and with industry analysts.

For high tech companies, the primary objective of a public relations campaign is to get some "ink": have an article written about your product in one or more trade publications, one that your customers will read. In a sense, an article is "free" advertising and is an effective way to build awareness of your new product.

Getting attention from the trade press can be accomplished in several ways. If you have an established relationship with certain publications, then you should call your contact to notify him or her about the upcoming new product that you are launching. If you don't have an established relationship or are targeting some new publications, then you may need an introduction through your public relations agency. That is a service that all agencies provide. Sometimes cold calling also may be effective, depending on how newsworthy your product might be.

It's a good idea to read trade magazines to get a feel for the types of coverage that companies receive in these publications. Sometimes companies only receive brief mention in articles that address important new trends in technology; other times companies can be the focus of an entire article.

For example, one company contacted a staff writer for a publication that focused on an industry that was a new target market for the company's products. The staff writer at the publication became excited about the product and company, and proposed a feature story on the new product. The company flew in several people to be interviewed by the writer. When the article was printed the following month, there was no mention whatsoever of the company or the product, for that matter.

There are no guarantees as to the extent of coverage you will receive; regardless of how strong your relationship may be with a trade press contact, what they publish is still at the whim of the writer and editor of the particular publication. If you can come up with an interesting angle about your product that will give the writer a new "hook", your chances of receiving coverage are significantly improved. The job of the trade press is to report on what's new and important in the particular industry that their publication covers. If you can help them do their job, they may give you some credit.

Writers of articles for trade press vary in their technical knowledge. Be prepared to explain your product functionality and benefits in the most basic and rudimentary terms. Messages must be clear and concise. Writers want to know what makes your product different from those of your competitors, along with what your overall strategy is for the product and the product line.

You may not have much time to get your point across, so any presentations that you make must be fairly brief. Typically, you will be lucky to get more than thirty minutes of time with the trade press to discuss your product. You can, however, compile supplementary material such as datasheets, white papers, and other types of collateral to leave with the writer that will provide reference material as he or she writes the article.

Some of the techniques used during public relations campaigns include issuing press releases, conducting press tours, and preparing press kits for distribution. Any or all of these help in getting your news to the trade press representatives that may result in press coverage.

Press releases

The most important document in a public relations campaign is the press release. A press release is a brief document from one to four pages long that announces a product or event to the newsrooms or offices of major print publications. The publications can then decide whether they want to do a news story or article based on the content of the release. Press releases are written by the corporate communications staff or a public relations group inside the company and are written in a journalistic style. A press release is sent out "over the wire", which today means the Internet or email, often sent out over a wireless network. Even though the technology involved in sending press releases has evolved from Teletype to fax to Internet and email, the basic format of a press release remains the same. Here are the basic parts:

Title- Must be engaging and newsworthy, contain keywords about what you're announcing, and be no more than two lines, in boldface type

City, (State), Date- followed by two dashes, and the first line of the body of the press release begins on the same line

Body – your story, divided into paragraphs, no more than two pages, usually has a quote from a company executive or a customer or both

Closing boilerplate – this is usually the "About the company" section that describes the company, where it's headquartered, its primary business, when it was founded, its website url, and any trademark information on products or company name

Contact information – Name, address, phone number, fax number, email address and web url for the company's press contact, there may be separate contact information if the company has a PR agency

In a press release, you want the product and company to sound as appealing as possible, so it's tempting to stretch the truth in order to draw more attention. However, remember that this information is going out to the external world, and you don't want any false claims out there that will get you into trouble. Therefore, err on the side of using descriptive words, backed up by facts, which describe how your products or company are unique or new or whatever your key message reflects.

Find out what your policies and procedures are inside your company regarding content of press releases. Pay attention to established procedures, because your company image is at stake. Nothing should go out over the wire unless it has been approved for release by all of the required reviewers, including the senior executives of the corporation, the communications department, and usually the legal department or outside legal counsel.

Press releases are usually posted to the company's website the same day that they are issued to the outside world. Most news wire services that serve business and technology now receive and archive press releases via the web.

Using Your Ink

Get ready to flaunt those hard-won articles in publications. Refer to the article in your other marketing materials, or provide a quote or excerpt. If the original article is in print media, request or purchase enough originals or reprints to stuff into press kits. Also get a copy of the electronic version and post it at the company website; draw attention to it from your homepage. If the article also lives elsewhere on the web, such as the website of the publication, post a link from your website to theirs; the publication will appreciate that and you will increase your good will with them. One note of caution: the publication's website may only post articles or keep them in archives for a certain period of time, so make sure that you find out how long it will be there; you don't want dead links from your website.

Press tours

Sometimes, press tours are set up as part of the public relations campaign. These are a series of brief meetings between executives or managers in your company and trade press or analysts. Press tours usually last a few days or a couple of weeks, and the company executives travel to the offices of the press and analysts. Public relations agencies set these up in advance for companies, using their established contacts within the industry, and agency personnel often accompany the executives during the tour.

Presentations that are prepared for press tours need to be carefully worded to capture the messages, to explain what the product does, and to do this using terminology that can be understood by the audience that is being addressed. It's a good idea to use customer quotes whenever possible, but be sure to get permission before using a customer's name. A good public relations agency can guide you through the process, but it's up to your company to develop the content and the messages that need to be carried forward. The agency can only help position the company with the press and analysts.

Press tours are a great way to receive immediate feedback about the product. Be sure to plan a review session with the participants of the tour as soon as it is completed. The primary objective of a press tour is to promote the new product and also the company. The result of the press tour is usually coverage in one or more trade publications. For that reason, press tours need to be well organized. Sufficient product and company information should be left with the press and analysts, so that they will have reference material for writing articles, should they choose to do so.

Press kits

Press kits are used primarily during a press tour, but they can also be used at trade shows or sent out to people who read the press release and need more information. Press kits may contain a variety of information. At a minimum, they should contain corporate background information such as facts and figures or history, the current press release and related recent press releases, copies of press presentations if used, datasheets or other collateral, and customer success stories or testimonials.

Industry and market analysts

Market research and industry analyst firms such as Gartner Group, Forrester, Yankee Group, IDC, Frost and Sullivan, and others focus on high tech companies and products. Receiving attention or coverage from these organizations can make or break a whole product launch campaign. Carefully think through the strategy of what you want to accomplish with your public relations campaign before you contact them. You may only get one chance to get their attention, and you want to maximize the opportunity.

There are many different reasons for working with analysts, depending on the company's strategic objectives. In some instances, you may only want to get the attention of analysts so that they will mention your product or company. Maybe they know your company pretty well, and are tired of hearing the same old story, so you might want to develop a new approach that will rejuvenate their interest. And occasionally analysts come looking for you because one of your competitors has just mentioned your company or product. It's a matter of defining your desired outcome, and building that into the strategy.

Many of these analyst and research organizations offer several levels of service to their clients, including consulting, primary market research, and marketing publications. Companies pay a lot of money to such companies to get confidential advice and feedback on new product strategies and positioning. Part of their service offering also includes subscriptions to their market research reports and analyses.

Analysts can have a lot of influence on market trends and can impact customers' buying behavior. Their opinion will make a difference in how your product is perceived in the overall marketplace. It's worthwhile to develop ongoing relationships with these organizations and to seek their counsel often.

Seminars and press conferences

Targeted seminars for press and analysts can be effective ways to educate people about your product in a group setting. These events are usually by invitation only, where you selectively invite people to participate. Seminars usually last no more than a few hours. They are a great opportunity to present more detailed information about the product and to do product demonstrations. Sometimes, seminars can be staged using web conferencing to facilitate remote participation. The most difficult challenge regarding seminars is gaining commitments from trade press and analysts to attend. Sometimes, a public relations agency may be needed to help implement these programs.

Press conferences can also be scheduled to increase the impact of your product announcement. These are often held during other major events such as trade shows, where there is likely to be a contingent of press and journalists on hand. During a press conference, key executives from the company give a brief presentation about the product and then answer questions from the press. Press kits are usually distributed as background information.

Timing of public relations campaigns

Ideally, public relations events such as press tours should take place the week before announcement date. Analysts and trade press like to have the scoop on a story before the rest of the general public reads the press release. Any advance information you can give them will be to your benefit in terms of obtaining coverage in publications.

The general availability date of your product may also be an important factor to consider. If you conduct a public relations campaign when your product won't be available for six months, trade press writers will not be too excited about writing about it. They don't like writing about "vaporware." This is especially true if you are doing a press tour. As a general rule of thumb, a press tour should take place no earlier than 30 days before product availability.

Seasons of the year can also play a part in public relations campaigns. There are a few "dead" seasons when it's difficult to schedule a press tour or even issue press releases. The summer, from mid-June to the end of August, is a time when a lot of people are on vacation and it's difficult to line up everyone that you may want to talk to on the tour. Another dead season is from Thanksgiving through the end of December. With all of the holidays and chaos, it's also very difficult to schedule a tour or major announcement.

Advertising

When someone mentions advertising, the first thing that people usually think of is a TV commercial. However, there's more to advertising than that. These days, there are many different forms and methods of advertising. Ads can appear in newspapers, magazines, journals, trade press, the Internet, and broadcast media such as television, cable, and radio. Web advertising has evolved over the last few years. Banner ads and pop-up ads were the early forms of web advertising, but were not always effective largely due to the annoyance factor. Now major search engine companies sell "ad words" that guarantee placement of the advertiser's website link on the search result return page or pages. The more the advertiser pays, the higher the placement on the list.

High tech companies traditionally did not use mass market advertising such as television or radio. That has changed in recent years. Sponsorships are also becoming more common; high tech companies are naming landmarks such as stadiums, as an opportunity to expand their brand awareness. Billboards are being used by high tech companies a lot more. Television ads for high tech products regularly appear during high profile events such as the Super Bowl, specials, and highly rated television shows. This is a new phenomenon. One of the reasons for this is that high tech companies have money to pay for such expensive advertising programs. Another reason is that there are many more markets for high technology products now, and potential customers are very widespread both demographically and geographically. This is true for the business-to-business market as well as the business to consumer market. If it's within your budget, advertising in some of these venues can be considered as a way to develop expanded awareness of your product and company. Figure 11.1 lists the key questions that need to be answered about advertising campaigns:

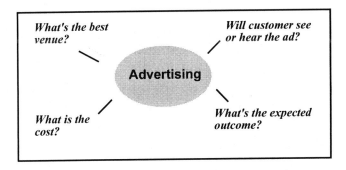

Figure 11.1 Key Questions About Advertising

Implementing an advertising campaign is fine, but everyone should be clear on the expected outcome of the campaign, and the company must realistically assess whether the target customer will hear or see the ad. Other considerations are the costs and the best venue for reaching customers.

There are many types of advertising that can be done during product launch. First, there may be an advertising campaign already going on in the company, and you might be able to leverage these efforts for your product. They may include radio, television or other broadcasting, web advertising, major newspapers or trade publications such as the Wall Street Journal, Fortune magazine, Business Week, and others. You may need to coordinate with the department or vendor who is doing the advertising campaign for the company, in order to identify how your product might fit in some of the advertisements already being planned.

You may also decide to develop an ad that is focused only on your product. The ad may be targeted for a special trade publication or some other media. Even if you develop separate ads at the product level, you need to coordinate the messages, tone, and style with any other advertising campaigns going on at the corporate level in order to be consistent. Product level ads can also help the corporate level campaign by further reinforcing the corporate level messages and image.

There are often opportunities to do targeted advertising in connection with events such as trade shows. Sometimes, trade publications will release a "conference issue" that they open up to additional advertisements for the trade show event. Usually, these ads also identify the booth number of the advertiser. If you can plan far enough in advance, this may be a worthwhile type of product level advertising.

If part of your objective is to reach a new vertical market, you may want to do some targeted advertising in a publication that serves that industry. Similarly, if you are trying to build up your awareness with distribution channels, you may want to look into advertising in trade publications that the channels use.

Timing of corporate level or product level advertising campaigns relative to launch date is problematic at best. If you plan to leverage the corporate level campaign, the date of the advertisements will be out of your control. These ads may appear before your product's marketing materials are ready. Sometimes, the ads appear several months after your launch, which may not have the impact you need for your product. In effect, the ad will be "old news". With a product level ad, you will have more control, but then you will have the problem of publication deadlines. For print ads, the deadlines will be thirty to sixty days in advance of publication. This means that in a three-month long product launch, you would need to begin work on the ad as one of the first tasks, if you want the ad to coincide with your launch date.

Most high tech companies contract with advertising agencies to develop and place ads. If companies have internal advertising groups, they are usually small departments that also work on marketing communications pieces, or they act as a liaison to the external ad agency.

Costs of public relations and advertising

Public relations and advertising campaigns can be quite expensive, especially if outside agencies are used. These programs are usually the most expensive line items in the marketing budget during product launch. It is advisable to plan these programs carefully and as far in advance as possible, in order to maximize the return on the investment that the company is making. The investment will be worth it, because it is through these programs that the market will become aware of your product.

12

Internal Marketing Programs

Internal marketing programs educate and inform the sales organization, customer support staff, employees, and occasionally, channel partners. These programs communicate information about the product being launched and the marketing strategy. Internal marketing programs can be quite complex and are just as important to the launch as external marketing programs. Companies take internal marketing very seriously, and most companies allocate a certain percentage of the marketing and sales budgets to fund these programs. Although companies have traditionally viewed the training of the sales organization as absolutely essential to revenue goals, more recently, companies have recognized the value in training all employees. Sufficient budget should be allocated to internal marketing programs, because without educating your employees, customer support staff, sales force, and channels, you will have little hope of selling your product.

Internal marketing programs are different than external marketing programs due to the company-confidential nature of the information and strategy inherent in internal marketing materials. Much can be communicated to employees and sales people about competitors, positioning, pricing, and strategic objectives that would not be appropriate to reveal to the outside world. Many different types of content can be included, depending on the audience. This chapter includes a table of the types of programs and intended audience.

Implementing internal marketing programs requires a coordinated effort across the company; several organizations need to be involved in the process. There are many different means of implementing these programs, from training sessions to the company intranet, to special events. Timing of internal marketing programs is critical, and these programs need to be rolled out in advance of the product announcement to the outside world.

Types of information to provide

During the average product launch, there is a lot of marketing information generated. You may have lengthy marketing plans, competitive analyses, message hierarchies, product specifications, press information, and pricing analyses. For the purposes of internal marketing, you don't need to provide everything on the list. Here is a checklist of what to provide for your internal audience:

   -Basic description of the product being launched and its relationship to other products or product families
   -Strategic objective for this product with respect to the company's business and market goals
   -Market strategy, including existing versus new customers being targeted and positioning relative to competitors, targeted geographies
   -List of competing companies and products and your company's differentiators
   -Pricing for the product
   -Key messages to be used during the selling process

-List and location of key sales collateral, documents or sales tools that can be used to help sell the product, including links to the company's internal and external websites

Sometimes you can assemble this key information in a single document like a marketing plan or launch plan that is placed on the company's internal network for access by employees, the sales force, or channel partners. Whether you have one document or several, it's important to use "version control" so that people are assured that they have the most current version of the documents. The various audiences and their needs are described in the next sections.

Internal marketing programs for the sales force

Sales people are the ultimate key to product launch success, so it's especially critical that marketing and sales work together effectively during launch. The line between the marketing and sales organizations is often blurry. Most marketing textbooks define marketing as a large collection of tasks and responsibilities: from market research to determine customer needs, to analysis of market size and trends, to formulation of strategy, to development of messages, to crafting promotional campaigns and creating marketing materials. The sales function is usually defined as merely one of the distribution channels to get the product to the target customer. But the reality is, even though sales people have a shorter job description, they are responsible for bringing in the revenue, and that is the most important objective in the entire marketing and sales cycle. Sales people have the most current, direct, and powerful interface with your customer, and without your customers, you don't have a business. Remember that the customer is the key individual in this whole process and they have the money!

The sales function is not easy. It takes time to turn long-shot cold calls or customer leads into revenue-producing customer relationships. Sales people must be excellent communicators, negotiators, and have the commitment to deliver what is promised – and keep the customer happy and smiling throughout the process. It's marketing's job to make the sales people successful, giving them the key information, sales materials and support they need when they need it, and especially during a product launch.

Internal marketing for the sales force is the most important and most complex type of internal marketing. The sales force needs up to the minute product information in order to do their jobs effectively. Sales representatives do not want to be in a selling situation where their customer prospect knows more about your company's products than they do. For that reason, companies of any size spend a substantial amount of time and money on sales training programs. Internal marketing programs for the sales force need to include all of the information that will be used for all employees, plus much more detailed information on how to sell and position the product against the competitors' products. There may also be detailed technical information about the product: how to configure it, how to price it, and how it will be supported. If any sales tools are developed, information on when and how to use them should be provided along with these tools.

It is difficult to find the proper medium for communicating this important information to the sales force. Sales people would much rather spend their time in front of customers than in front of an instructor. The most successful type of sales training program is that which will allow a sales person to remain mobile while learning. Multimedia programs such as the intranet, CD, and interactive webcasts are ways to minimize training time.

Sales people can essentially learn at their own pace, when they have the time.

To be effective, the sales force needs to have specialized selling information, configuration and pricing guides, and various types of sales tools. Often, the various types of information and materials are packaged into sales kits. Sales representatives need presentations that they can use with customer prospects. The presentations need to be ready for the sales force on the launch date, if not before. Sales people need enough time to learn the material and develop speaking notes for the slides. Detailed competitive and positioning information should be made available to the sales force so that they can be armed with the most recent information regarding the competing products and be more prepared to address specific product differentiators in selling situations.

Internal marketing programs for the customer support organization

Generally speaking, a product should not be launched without adequate plans in place for post-sales support. Customer support should have its own plan, in keeping with the "whole product" concept, which includes the set of related support functions required to deliver the product to the end user customer. This may seem like an obvious requirement, but many high tech products are routinely launched without adequate planning in this area. For example, one company launched a major new product line to a new market segment and assumed the company's support organization would provide technical support to the customers. The organization did provide support to the customers, but so did the channel partners - for the same product and for the same customers! The customers were totally confused about whom to contact for support. Had this been resolved prior to launch, it would have prevented a very embarrassing situation, not to mention the extra expense of two separate support organizations providing the same service.

The customer support organization can be a valuable conduit for customer feedback on recently launched products. The product marketing team should make it a priority to request feedback on recently launched products from the customer support team. Feedback might consist of tech support issues with the product, or suggestions, or problems in using the product for its intended application. Other key information can also be obtained, such as how the customer learned about the company and product, or what they like about the product. Product marketers should do this before developing additional products in the product line, and before they launch the next product in the series. Not only will they know which marketing programs to use, but they will also know which features or functionality to emphasize or de-emphasize, as the case may be. Product marketers might also be able to find customers to use for success stories, case studies or quotes. This improves the overall customer relationship, making the customer feel that they are important to the company.

When the launch plan is put into place, the customer support organization should be fully aware of the product being launched and when it will be launched. They will need a lot of advance notice to prepare for this and may need special training on how to handle customer inquiries. Not only does this include technical training about the product, but also how it is positioned in the market. Your customer support organization provides a unique interface directly to your customer, and so they need to understand the importance of this product to the company. Of particular interest is whether they will be interfacing with new types of customers, and also how to promote the new product in the course of providing support services for other products. Some customer support representatives are also trained to help promote and sell new products. If that is the case in your company, you may need to develop some selling materials similar to those used for the sales force. This material needs to be concise and usable as a quick reference, because support representatives have to be able to refer to it while they are on the phone with customers.

Internal marketing programs for all employees

Everyone in your company is responsible for marketing the company's products, whether or not marketing is part of his or her job description. All employees need to know in advance about new products being launched and the relative importance of each product to the company's overall strategy. To the extent that it's possible to have product demonstrations for all employees, it is highly advisable to conduct such events. Internal marketing programs for other employees (besides the sales and customer support organization) include multimedia events and all-hands meetings, email and intranet communications, and newsletters. Some companies have regular "open houses" or mini-tradeshows for employees to educate them on products that are being launched.

The purpose of these programs is to get sufficient high-level product information to all employees, along with an explanation of the strategic objectives of the product, so that employees can understand the positioning. Every employee should be aware of new products and what they mean to the company and should be able to act as a spokesperson in that regard.

Internal marketing programs for all employees need to include a description of the product and its functionality and features, the competitors, the positioning statements, the corporate-level and product-level marketing messages, and the channel marketing strategy. Additionally, information should be included on corporate business objectives relative to the product.

Employees need to have new product information before the launch date or the press announcement. Sometimes in the rush of trying to get everything done during a launch, the internal marketing falls to the bottom of the priority list and is left until the last minute. With the widespread availability of corporate intranets and email, the task of briefing the employees can now be done very quickly.

Communication of strategic objectives is an essential part of internal marketing. All employees need to understand the relationship between the product being launched and the corporate direction. Sometimes, positioning statements are articulated directly to employees or are put in the form of an email sent by one of the officers or senior managers of the company.

Basic product information such as datasheets or white papers should also be made available to employees so that they know the basic functionality of the product and customer benefits.

Internal marketing programs for channels

Marketing programs for channels sometimes have more of an internal focus than an external focus. Channel agreements may specify co-marketing programs or sharing of certain levels of marketing materials that are more proprietary than collateral distributed to the outside world. Companies will often allow limited access to their intranet for established channel partners that sell or reuse the company's products. It's in the company's best interest to share selling strategies and tools with channel partners, as long as that information is not leaked to competitors. The way to protect this information is usually through the channel partnering agreement.

Internal marketing programs for channels are usually delivered over the corporate intranet, with special password-protected access set up for selected channel partners. Information for channels is only at the product level and includes technical information on how to configure the product and how it will be supported. How to sell and price the product is normally left up to the channel partner, but this information is sometimes made available as well.

Guidelines for content distribution

In the preceding paragraphs, many different types of programs and content were discussed. The table on the following page can be used as a general guide for planning different materials and programs for each of the four types of intended audiences.

Program or Type of Material	Sales force	Customer support	All employees	Channel partners
Sales training	x			x
Sales kits and tools	x	x		x
Webcasts	x			x
Corporate intranet announcements	x	x	x	x
All-hands meetings, presentations	x	x	x	
Multimedia material (CDs)	x			x
Email	x	x	x	x
Newsletters	x	x	x	x
Datasheets, white papers and collateral	x	x	x	x
Pricing guides	x			x
Sales presentation	x			
Marketing plan, strategy	x	x	x	
Advance press release	x	x	x	

Who's responsible for implementing internal marketing programs?

There are many organizations in the company that need to be involved in implementing internal marketing programs. The launch team fulfills a very important role in this regard. Each member of the team should consider himself or herself an ambassador for the product. Since launch teams should be made up of representatives of cross-functional organizations, they can carry this information to their own functional organizations within the company as the launch progresses.

If the company has a corporate communications group, it may be part of their charter to develop internal communications programs and events to educate employees on new products. Find out if there is such a group, and get them involved in helping to plan a program for your launch.

The sales training group will usually have the greatest responsibility for internal marketing: training the sales force about the new product. Depending on the size of the company, these groups can be fairly large and have formalized procedures for sales curricula development and delivery of training classes, scheduled up to one year in advance. The earlier that you can meet with the sales training group, the better. It may be difficult to find a window of time during which you can train the sales force. If your launch date is in between regularly scheduled training events, you may have to do the training well in advance of the launch or after the launch. Sometimes, you may need to develop other ways to provide training to the sales force besides in-person training sessions, such as intranet-based training, webcasts, or mobile training modules on CD. These programs take time to develop, and that's why early coordination with the sales training organization is recommended.

The human resources department may also be involved in product training, especially as part of an orientation course for new employees. You should find out how often they update the orientation program, and your product needs to be part of the content. In some companies, the human resources department has broad responsibilities for all types of employee training, including technical training about new products. If that is the case, you should meet with them to identify ways to get your new product information included in the training programs.

Product development organizations also need to be updated on the release of new products. Quite often, these organizations also have training responsibilities for their technical staff. Sometimes informal "brown bag" meetings and presentations are held to regularly update the technical staff on new products.

Vehicles for internal marketing programs

Today, the most common way to distribute information to the employees and sales force is the corporate intranet (as discussed in Chapter 10). Access can be controlled via password and network administration, so it is a reasonably secure way to distribute company-internal marketing data. Sometimes, companies may be too small to have an intranet, or may have one but don't have the resources in place to add and update content. In those situations, the most common electronic form of communication is the use of email. Some email programs allow shared folders that multiple users can access. This is a good place to post drafts of various marketing materials to facilitate review and feedback. It's also a good place to post the final versions of marketing materials that will serve as reference documents that can be accessed after the launch.

Email can be used to distribute "letters" or announcements from the executives to all employees. These email messages often contain personalized versions of the corporate messages that pertain to the product being launched. Messages sent from executives are often motivational in tone, designed to create momentum and enthusiasm among the employees.

Companies are increasingly turning to multimedia vehicles for implementing internal marketing programs. The cost of using various media has decreased, making it easier to justify. Multimedia programs also enable the company to reach more people more quickly. Today, companies routinely use CDs and webcasts to reach employees and the sales force.

Timing of internal marketing programs

Internal marketing programs must be ready to go before the announcement date or launch date for the product. Some information can be distributed a few weeks in advance, such as sales presentations, the positioning, and messages. Some companies also make the marketing plan available to employees.

Distribution of the press release is usually made to the employees the same day of the release to the general public, but usually a few hours before the external release. The press release is also usually posted to the company's website and intranet on the day of release. If a press tour was conducted before the general press release, any feedback from the press or announcements of anticipated trade press articles should be posted for employees at the same time as the press release.

Employees and the sales force may receive early copies of product collateral. These usually are distributed with a warning not to print or give directly to customers, however, until the print or web versions are finalized.

Employees need to know the various venues for external marketing that are planned for the product, especially any future trade shows. The more notice that employees have to educate themselves about new products, the better prepared they will be to help market the product.

If implemented correctly, internal marketing programs can help supplement your overall marketing efforts to launch your product. It pays to take the time to develop a set of comprehensive internal marketing programs as part of your marketing and launch plans.

Now that you have an idea of which external and internal marketing programs you plan to pursue, they can be compiled in the marketing plan document, the subject of Chapter 13.

13

The Marketing Plan

The marketing plan is the master plan that defines the product, customer, market, and strategy, and lists all of the marketing programs that will be executed during the implementation phase of the product launch. The marketing plan can be written by the product manager or the launch team, but the content needs to be reviewed by all of the organizations involved in launching the product. In addition, there is often a requirement that the senior marketing executive in the company approve marketing plans before they are implemented.

Companies use the marketing plan as the reference document to guide them through the development of the launch plan, which in turn will guide the launch implementation. The marketing plan's list of marketing programs and deliverables determines the tasks that are in the launch plan and schedule. Marketing plans are not static documents. As market conditions change, the marketing plan should be continually updated to position the product in the best possible way at the time of launch implementation. The launch team needs to be fully aware of any changes made to the plan so that the launch plan can be modified accordingly.

Marketing plan content

The marketing plan defines the strategy for getting your product to the market, as well as the tactical steps you will take to implement the strategy. The marketing plan document contains all the product, market, customer, and channel characterizations that were developed in the earlier stages of the launch. The competitive analysis and positioning needs to be captured in the plan, along with the FAB chart and list of differentiators. The various levels of messages need to be identified. All of the marketing programs should be listed, including internal and external programs, public relations, and advertising. Figure 13.1 shows how all of the elements are combined in the marketing plan.

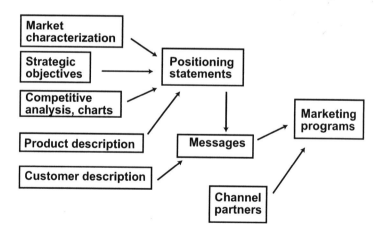

Each element is also included as a section in the marketing plan

Figure 13.1 Elements of the Marketing Plan

All of the sections of the plan need to be woven together along with the overall strategy for the product. Anyone reading the plan should have a clear idea of the product that is being launched, the market environment for launch, and how the product will be introduced and promoted to the target market.

Marketing plan template

The following is a template for a marketing plan that has been used successfully for many product launches. The template includes the required sections of the plan, and for each section, there are questions that need to be answered in order to develop and write the plan. This format works well because it forces the plan writer to think through the plan, prompted by the questions.

The marketing plan may be very brief and concise, or long and detailed. The length of the document is not as important as the content. As long as all of the questions are addressed, the marketing plan will contain all of the necessary information.

Marketing Plan Template

1) Executive Summary
Summarizes the main points of the plan; usually one page in length. This is written last, after all of the other sections have been filled in.

2) Strategic Business Objectives
This section addresses the company's strategic objective for the product. What does the company want to achieve with this product? Enter a new market? Keep up with the competition? Have renewed visibility in the same market? Effect a change

of image? Use the product to turn around the company financially?

3) Product or Service Description

What does the product do, or what is the service offering? What is the function and application of the product? Include a picture or diagram where possible so that the reader can quickly grasp the concepts. List major features of the product or service. What role does product play in the overall product roadmap or strategy for the company?

4) Target Customer Description

Who is a typical customer for this product? What is their level of authority in the buying organization? What is the customer problem that the product or service will solve? Who are their customers? Articulate the customer's compelling reason to buy your product or service, and the value proposition for the customer.

5) Market Trends

What are the market trends that affect this product? Is the market dying, growing, or emerging?

6) Market Segments and Size

Which market segments are you targeting? Explain the different customers and required distribution channels for each segment. How large is the market for your product? The information should be described quantitatively. A TAM-SAM-SOM analysis can be done in this section (total available market, served available market, share of market). The projections should go out five years if possible. What is the company's targeted sales forecast for the product? What would the level of sales need to be in order to attain the desired percent of market share?

7) Competition

What is the competitive environment? Who are the competitors for the product? The competitors should be described by name, competing products, price position, and marketing and selling strategy. A competitive matrix should be included that characterizes the company and product, feature by feature relative to the competition. What are your key differentiators at the company and product level?

8) Market Strategy

What is the high level strategy you will follow for this product? How does this strategy assure you competitive advantage?

9) Pricing

What is the pricing strategy for the product or service? What are the revenue projections for the product in terms of the overall corporate-level objectives? What is the pricing sensitivity of your customers?

10) Positioning

-Price Positioning. How does your price compare to your competitors' products?

-Competitive Positioning. What are the differentiators at a product level and at a corporate level compared to your competitors? What is your added value? Include a competitive matrix and FAB chart in this section.

11) Business Model and Distribution Channels

How will you get your products to the customer? Include a business model map showing channels and the supply chain if applicable. Will you only use the direct sales force, or will you use established or new indirect channels? Who are the existing channel partners, and will they sell your product? If new channel partners need to be developed, what is the plan for engaging them? What marketing materials will your channel partners need?

12) Strategic Partners

Other than channel partners, are there other external organizations involved in the process of getting your product to market? These can include marketing partners, OEMs, investment partners, or joint development partners. Who are they and what role will they play in the overall marketing plan?

13) Messaging

What are the corporate level and product level messages for the product? How will the messages be used in the various marketing programs that are planned? Include the hierarchy of messages in this section.

14) Marketing Programs

What marketing programs will be used to get the messages to your target customer? For each of the following major categories, describe what deliverables are planned:

-External Marketing (direct mail, web, seminars, trade shows, events)

-Collateral (data sheets, brochures, white papers, multimedia, presentations, application notes, success stories, web versions)

-Public Relations and Advertising

-Internal Marketing (sales communications, guides, tools, training, intranet)

15) Customer Service and Support Plan

How will the product be supported? Who is the responsible group or channel partner? How will value-added service/support be sold and positioned? How is it priced and bundled with the product? Will the customer support organization be encouraged to help sell the new product?

16)Sales and Channel Training Plan

How will the sales force be educated about the product? Who will develop the course curriculum and deliver the training, and via what vehicle? What will be the training schedule? What sales events can be leveraged during product rollout? How will you educate your channel partners on the product? What vehicle will you use to train your partners? How will your indirect channel partners know when to sell your product instead of your competitor's?

17) Risk Analysis and Mitigation
What are the risks of executing the marketing plan, and how can these risks be mitigated? Possible risks are:
-Slip in date of product release
-Competitor announcing product before you do
-Indirect channel doesn't sell product
-Inadequate funding to do everything in the plan
Describe a contingency plan for the risks that are most likely in your particular company environment.

Process for generating the plan

Generating a marketing plan means gathering together all of the information about the product, customer, and market, and then writing the plan according to an outline or a template such as the one in this chapter. It may be useful to gather a team together to assemble the background information and input, and then use a brainstorming session to go through the template questions together.

This will be a useful exercise for the cross-functional team members in terms of preparing them to participate in the implementation phase of the launch. Using a team approach will also enable you to get several opinions regarding how to interpret the background information, as well as the strategy that ties everything together.

Once the basic questions are answered, then a draft of the plan should be written and distributed to several organizations for review. Comments should be incorporated, and the document should then be finalized for distribution. Some companies also require that a designated senior manager approve the plan before it is widely distributed.

How the marketing plan is used

Decision-makers and launch team members use a marketing plan in different ways. Figure 13.2 shows the uses of the plan by these constituencies.

Corporate decision-makers	**Product/launch team**
-How much budget do I need to allocate to this product? *-How important is this product to the company?* *-Are the programs appropriate, given the market size/trends?* *-Will the market strategy maximize competitive advantage?* *-Which partners need to be on board and when?* *-What will the sales force need to know to sell this new product?* *-What publicity is needed and what is the fit with corporate PR plans?* *-What do our employees need to know about this new product?* *-What are the key messages?* *-What are the risks and how can we mitigate them?*	*-What is the product we are marketing?* *-How important is this product to the company?* *-How difficult will it be to create and sustain our competitive advantage?* *-Do we know this customer, and do we know these competitors?* *-Will we need to work with any new partners during the launch?* *-What key messages need to be used in all programs?* *-Which programs are we going to implement during launch, and when?*

Figure 13.2 How Different Constituencies Use the Plan

It is important to keep this in mind when writing the plan in order to allow for the appropriate type of content that each person will need. However, don't make the plan too long and detailed or no one will read it. The more concise the plan, the more useful it will be as a reference. Most of the sections of the marketing plan can be summarized in tables, charts or bulleted lists. Most marketing plans are from 10 to 20 pages long at the most.

Updating the marketing plan

There may be old marketing plans available for the product that can be updated or serve as a framework for generating the new plan. Often, a marketing plan is generated during the early stages of the new product cycle, before the product is developed. This is sometimes called a marketing "spec" or a marketing requirements document. If a plan was done at that time, it's a good idea to obtain a copy of it. There may be some useful information in it that can be used for the new marketing plan. A marketing plan that was done in that stage of the cycle usually will have defined the customer needs and specifications that your company used in building the product. Sometimes these plans are one to two years old, and the market conditions, as well as the competitors, will likely have changed. The market information and competitive analysis from the old plan will not be useful for the new marketing plan; however, the customer value proposition may still be valid. You should identify the specific customer needs that the product was supposed to address, and then you should talk with the product development group to find out if anything has changed during the development phase.

Once the new marketing plan has been written, reviewed, and approved, it needs to be updated during the launch implementation phase if market conditions change. The plan should be updated when any of the following events occur during the launch phase:

> -New competitors emerge
> -Competitors announce new products similar to yours
> -Your company engages new channel partners
> -New functionality of the product is discovered during beta testing
> -Your company announces major new strategic directions

Any business or market condition that affects your strategy or marketing programs should trigger an update of your marketing plan. Marketing plans need to be flexible so that they can accommodate the rapid pace of change inherent in high tech markets.

Communicating changes in the marketing plan

All of the organizations involved in generating the marketing plan and supporting the product launch should be notified of changes in the plan. Electronic versions of the plan can be made available in shared folders that reside on the corporate network, with controlled access for key launch team members. Any updates to the plan should trigger a change in how the plan is labeled. To keep track of different versions of the plan, add a date and time stamp in the header or footer of the document, or assign a version number to the plan. That way, all readers will know whether they have the most current version. People also need to know the reason for the change or what triggered the change so that they better understand the impact on the marketing plan. Sometimes, substantive changes in the plan require another review and approval cycle on the part of management. If that is the case, then management should review the changed content first, before it is distributed to the team.

Relationship between the marketing plan and the launch plan

The marketing plan content becomes an input to the launch plan. The marketing programs described in the plan and the deliverables list determines the tasks that need to be done in the launch implementation phase. It is important that any updates or changes made to the marketing plan be communicated to the person responsible for the launch plan, so that changes in the tasks, resources, and schedule can be made accordingly.

PART III

Launch Planning
and Implementation

14

The Launch Planning Process

Now that the marketing work of the launch is complete, it's time to begin the project management phase. This includes detailed launch planning and managing the implementation of the launch. A carefully planned launch will be much easier to manage. It pays to take the time to think through and document all of the details of the human resources, the schedule, and the budget necessary to implement the launch. Effective launch management requires solid project management skills and effective communications with all organizations involved in the launch. The launch manager has responsibility for the people, budgets, deliverables and the schedule for the launch; that's a lot to track and manage during a very chaotic time.

Timing of Launch Planning

The launch plan should be in place at least two months before the launch date, and three months of lead time is even better. Some of the launch deliverables may take several weeks to develop, so you may need extra time in the schedule. In addition, the launch plan may need upper management approval before the work can begin, which can mean a delay of days or sometimes weeks. Before this effort can begin, the following key tasks must first be completed:

-Strategic objectives have been identified for the launch
-The launch date has been determined
-All messages have been defined and approved
-Detailed description of the product is available
-The marketing plan has been completed and approved
-Budget for the launch has been approved

Who prepares the launch plan?

In most cases, the person who will be the launch manager prepares the launch plan. If the person has prior experience with launches, he or she will have a very good idea of the time required to produce deliverables or who should be assigned to them. That experience reduces the time that it takes to create the plan. If the planner becomes the launch manager, then there is no learning curve involved and the work can begin sooner. In some situations, however, there may be someone who prepares the plan and then it is handed off to a different person to manage the launch, such as a product manager. In that case, there should be some interaction between the two individuals during the planning process to set expectations and to make sure that the plan makes sense.

Sources of information for launch planning

There are several major sources of information that will need to be available in order to begin launch planning. The marketing plan should be complete and available; this will contain the list of external and marketing programs that make up the launch deliverables. The list of launch resources needs to be established, including who will serve on the launch team, and names of employees and any outside vendors who will be involved in producing or supporting launch deliverables. Sometimes those that serve on the launch team are in an advisory capacity and sometimes they are also responsible for producing specific launch deliverables, so all human resources should be listed along with their anticipated role in the launch. Schedule information needs to be obtained from other organizations within the company, including the official launch date, dates of events such as trade shows that may occur during the launch, and dates of planned press or analyst tours and advertising campaigns. The total budget for the launch needs to be obtained from the marketing department, product group, or whatever functional organization is the cost center for the launch. These sources of information combine in a series of planning steps to create the major pieces of the launch plan, as shown in Figure 14.1:

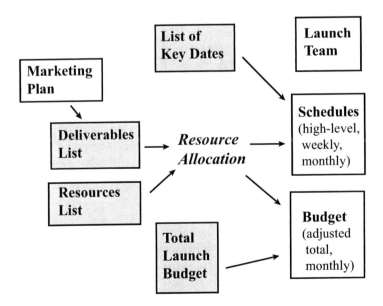

Figure 14.1 Compiling the Launch Plan

Organizing the work

The planning process can be challenging. There is a lot of information to assimilate in a short time and pressure to create a meaningful plan that makes sense and that people can easily follow. The next three chapters will guide you through three steps of the plan: assembling the launch team, allocating resources and determining the schedule, and allocating the launch budget. Chapter 18 illustrates how to compile the elements into a launch plan that can be used to manage the launch day to day.

15

The Launch Team

Early in the launch planning process, the key people who will do the work during the launch phase must be identified, and the launch team needs to be formed. The ideal launch team includes individuals from several organizations inside the company, and sometimes it includes individuals from outside the company. In other words, the launch team must be "cross-functional". The team should be made up of all the people necessary to implement the identified marketing programs, along with a capable team leader to act as launch manager. Sometimes, launch teams are referred to as "virtual teams", because the team members serve only during the launch, and then disband.

Who needs to be on the launch team?

Composition of a launch team depends on the size of the organization and the number of departments that are required to support a launch. In some companies, there are specific organizations responsible for managing product launches, such as central marketing, product management, sales, or business development. Regardless of where the organizational responsibility lies, a great degree of cross-functional coordination is always necessary to implement a product launch. Figure 15.1 illustrates the six organizations that need to work together for a successful launch.

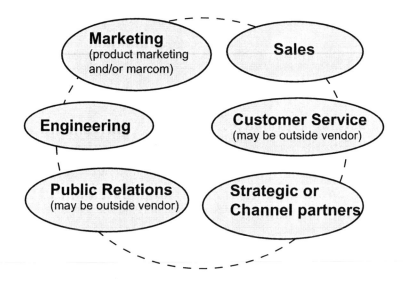

Figure 15.1 Launch Team Representation

Product launches require that the two groups who get along least well in the organization - engineering and marketing - work together seamlessly as a virtual team. Sometimes the marketing function is part of a centralized group within the company, and often includes the marketing communications staff. Product marketing staff may be located in product or development groups. Public relations may be handled internally or outsourced to a P.R. vendor. The sales organization really needs to be involved throughout the launch in order to provide feedback about existing customers and also to provide recommendations on marketing and sales materials. The customer service organization should also be included so that they will be up to date in supporting the new product. Strategic or channel partners also should participate in the launch team if possible to provide guidance on channel marketing programs for the launch.

The ideal launch team has representatives from all six organizations. At a bare minimum, the launch team needs to have representatives from marketing, engineering, sales, and public relations. You can build your launch team from there, and include others who will support the launch. A safe rule of thumb is to include a representative from every group who will be involved in creating a deliverable for the launch. A representative from senior management who can speak to corporate strategy issues should be on the team, at least in an advisory capacity. This person should have enough authority to speak for senior management regarding corporate messaging and strategic objectives.

If the company has a central marketing department, representatives who can review and approve external marketing communications should be on the team as well. Sometimes, all of the marketing deliverables are created internally. If so, representatives from the internal marketing communications staff should be on the launch team so that the deliverables and deadlines can be communicated back to the support staff in order to ensure that the launch project stays on track. If there is a separate market research or competitive analysis organization in the company, they also need to send a representative.

There may be a need to include international representatives on the launch team. Very few product launches these days are limited to North America. Fueled by the Internet, the high tech world is global, like it or not. The only reason not to announce your product globally might be that your product is not technologically compatible with the infrastructure in other countries; in that case, you will by necessity be limited to those regions where the product is functional. Coordination with international offices is necessary during product launch. Collateral that is developed for the launch may need to be translated and reprinted in different sizes for use in other countries. Channel programs are very different and more prevalent in many other parts of the world (such as Europe) than they are in North America. Sales training and customer events need to be coordinated for other countries. Messaging may need to be different if there are different competitors in other countries. The best way to manage these differences is to involve representatives from international offices very early in the process, in order to facilitate a smooth transition from the North American marketing programs to the international programs.

Choosing a launch manager

Appointing a launch manager (sometimes called a program manager or project manager) is the first step in forming a team. The launch manager acts as the point of contact between product development, marketing, and any outside vendors. He or she coordinates all the communications and interactions among launch team members and key suppliers. The launch manager is accountable for maintaining the launch schedule, managing the budget, and ensuring that the team completes all deliverables. The individual needs to be skilled in team building and project management, leadership, decision-making, facilitation, and communications in order to be an effective launch manager.

In most organizations, the product manager has ultimate responsibility for the product launch, although that individual may not be the launch manager. Sometimes the central marketing organization supplies a launch manager to the product development group. Regardless of which group the launch manager comes from, he or she needs to act independently and objectively while making decisions and leading the team. The launch manager should not favor one department or organization over another.

Even in the best of circumstances, disputes arise during this critical and stressful time. It is important that the person who has been selected as the team leader be empowered to manage any disputes or to escalate issues further up the organization until they are resolved.

Building the team

Startup or small companies might not have enough people in the organization to form a launch team with one representative from each functional area. It may be necessary in that instance to make sure that the people who are on the team take all of these functional perspectives into consideration. This means that a very few individuals will wear many hats, or that external vendors and consultants need to be brought in on a short-term basis during the launch.

Sometimes, in order to assign someone to the launch team, it will be necessary to obtain the approval of the person's functional manager. Usually, however, managers realize the importance of product launch and will try to make someone available from their organization for the launch team.

In putting together a launch team, it is important that prospective members be made to understand that they are committing to a chaotic and demanding project. If individuals have not served on a launch team before, it is best to prepare them ahead of time. Otherwise, you run the risk of having people abandon the effort halfway through the launch.

The launch manager must also assign roles to the launch team members. The function of the team as a whole is to handle the transition of the product when it comes out of the development cycle, and get the product released into the marketplace.

As part of that effort, the sales people have to know about the product and how to sell it, and need information and tools to help sell it. The external marketplace needs to become aware of the product, and be compelled to purchase it. All of that involves the assembly and communication of a lot of information: the launch deliverables.

Assuming a team with five members, here is one way to divide up the work:

-Sales Liaison - maintain contact with the sales organization (and especially sales training) to make sure that they receive the right marketing materials and sales tools to sell the product
-P.R. Liaison - act as a liaison with any public relations organization (internal or external) to develop and distribute press releases as needed
-Engineering representative – Report status of product release and availability, provide detailed descriptions of product features and functionality for marketing materials, gather information for sales training on the product, provide to team the results of any beta testing and customer feedback
-Marketing communications – coordinate and develop marketing materials such as datasheets, brochures, web content, sales training kits, and other materials
-Launch team leader: Must meet regularly with team to obtain status on all activities, report progress to management, plan and manage all deliverables, maintain budget

Timing

The launch team should be ready to go at least two months before launch. Some of the team members may provide information that is needed to complete the launch plan, such as product managers who know the beta testing schedule or product availability dates. If you can assemble the launch team even earlier, such as three or four months prior to launch, some of the team members can also help during the data gathering phase of launch, such as conducting market analysis or formulating customer descriptions. The earlier in the process that people are involved, the greater contribution they will make as the launch is implemented because they will already be familiar with the product and the target market.

When the launch team is in place, then the individuals need to be assigned to tasks, and the schedule can be developed, as discussed in Chapter 16.

16

The Launch Schedule and Resource Allocation

As described in Chapter 14, the launch plan is driven by the deliverables list in the marketing plan, and then resources are assigned to the schedule consistent with the budget and schedule of key dates. We will address that part of the process in this chapter. The starting point is the deliverables list in the marketing plan; this defines what needs to be done so that you can determine who will do the work and when.

The deliverables list

The list of deliverables is taken from the marketing plan, and includes all of the marketing materials that will be created during the launch phase and all of the marketing programs, including the details of the public relations and advertising campaigns that will be implemented. The marketing programs and deliverables should be grouped into internal marketing and external marketing programs, and then should be further broken down into categories such as collateral, public relations, and advertising.

Each deliverable may require the work of several individuals in order to complete it. For instance, a datasheet will require a writer, an editor, a reviewer, a graphic designer and printer. These are usually different individuals who perform a specific task.

Therefore, each deliverable on your list will likely require that the work flows from one individual to the next, each of whom will perform his or her task and then hand it off to another individual who will perform his or her task. When everyone has completed his or her individual tasks, then the deliverable can be considered complete.

The Resource Allocation Table

In order to develop a resource allocation table, you will first need to identify all of the people who will perform work on the launch. At a minimum, these will include the people on your assembled launch team, but there may be others as well who support the deliverables behind the scenes. List the people by function rather than by name; this will enable you to more easily identify the tasks that they will perform during the launch process. Here is an example:

-Product Manager- provide source content for deliverables, review collateral, participate in press tour, train sales force

-Market research analyst - gather pricing data, analyze competitors, gather market size data

-Copy writer - write text for collateral and sales presentations

-Editor - edit all copy

-Printer - print all collateral

-Public Relations firm - write press releases, develop press campaign, provide press feedback and analysis, recommend best time for announcement

-Webmaster - post press releases and collateral to company website

-Trade show manager - arrange for booth space for product, identify best tradeshows to attend

-Sales training department - provide templates for sales training content, incorporate product information into training sessions

-Channel marketing organizations - identify collateral needed to inform channels about product

-International representative - identify collateral to be translated or reprinted, modify press material for local markets

The next step is to assign people to each of the specific tasks under each deliverable. Each deliverable should be listed in a "People/deliverables" spreadsheet or table, and then each task should be assigned an "owner", the person responsible for making sure that the task is completed. When the spreadsheet is complete, it becomes the first draft of the resource allocation table.

Deliverables/ People	Datasheet	White Paper	Sales tool CD
Product Manager	Outline, provide content	Review	Develop content
Contract writer	Write	Write	Write text content
Corporate editor	Edit	Edit	Edit text content
Graphic designer	Develop illustrations	Develop illustrations	Develop artwork
Printer	Print	Print	
Multimedia producer			Record and edit CD

Table 16.1 Resource Allocation

Assigning task owners will enable you to identify gaps in resources; if there are no names that you can list in the table then you must find someone to fill the gap. Outside vendors or contractors may be needed to fill these gaps. Sometimes, the resource allocation table may indicate an overload of tasks for particular individuals. In that case, extra help may be needed for those deliverables. Table 16.1 is an example of a resource allocation table.

When you are at this stage of resource allocation, it's a good idea to assemble budget information for each deliverable, such as bids from outside vendors or number of hours to do tasks. This will save time when you assemble the budget using the guidelines in Chapter 17.

The primary advantage of using a table format such as this is that it explicitly shows the handoff or interface points between team members. This information will be useful when the launch schedule is developed.

Once you have completed the initial draft of the resource allocation table, you're ready to assign specific individuals to team roles. Let's suppose that you know who will work on the tasks inside the company. You can fill in the names next to the tasks in the table. Similarly, when you have identified the outside vendors who will provide the services that you are missing, you can name as well. Here is the same table with the persons' names filled in:

Deliverables/ People	Datasheet	White Paper	Sales tool CD
Product Manager- Eric Smith	Outline, provide content	Review	Develop content
Contract writer- Miriam Hammer	Write	Write	Write text content
Corporate editor- Sally Horvath	Edit	Edit	Edit text content
Graphic designer- Amy Pixel	Develop illustrations	Develop illustrations	Develop artwork
Printer- Wordsmith Printing	Print	Print	
Multimedia producer- LiveArts			Record and edit CD

Table 16.2 Resource Allocation with Names

When you have filled in the chart for all of the deliverables in a similar fashion, you will be able to identify the people who may need some help. In the above example, Miriam Hammer and Amy Pixel are going to very busy people, along with the corporate editor, Sally Horvath. You may need to arrange for additional resources for the tasks, but before you do that, you need to determine if the tasks will overlap in time. You need to develop the schedule first.

The launch schedule

Once the resources are allocated to the required tasks, the launch schedule can be developed. The first step is to compile a one-page launch timeline with all of the launch deliverables on one page, as shown in Figure 16.1.

This timeline lists all major launch milestones and serves as a baseline for developing more detailed launch schedules in the form of spreadsheets for all of the deliverables. The launch milestones from the timeline become the deadline dates for deliverables in the detailed launch schedules.

The detailed launch schedule shows all of the deliverables and the tasks needed to complete them, the stop and start dates for the major tasks, and overlaps and dependencies between tasks.

The timeline should start at the launch kickoff meeting, and should end one month past the launch date in order to capture all of the deliverables associated with the launch. Each major task involved in creating deliverables and programs should have a task line on the schedule. In addition, the major milestones should be plotted on this schedule, including the launch date and the launch kickoff date.

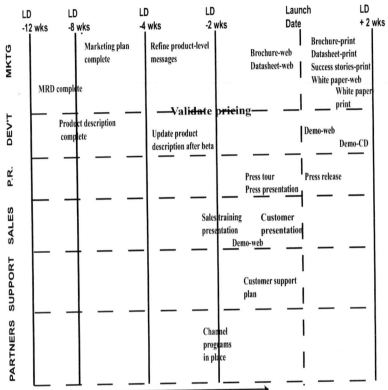

Figure 16.1 The Launch Timeline

In addition, you will also need to plot the dates of any key corporate events that will require involvement of the launch team, or events that you need to leverage in terms of promotional opportunities for the launch. You should also obtain a list of the trade shows that your company will be participating in during the launch phase.

The most critical milestone in any product launch is the launch date. All of the deliverables will be scheduled relative to the launch date. Most of the deliverables will need to be done before the launch date, but there are usually some that will follow within a few weeks. The first thing you need to do it to calculate the completion date for each deliverable, relative to the launch date. The next thing to do is to calculate the "cycle time" for each task, based on your company's history. How long does it take to do a piece of collateral or to develop a sales presentation? You need to find out the average cycle time, so that you can determine the start date for each task.

You can develop schedules using special scheduling or project management software packages if you like. They are set up to quickly calculate and plot events on a baseline schedule. If you do not have such software, you can use a simple table like the one that follows, and then draw a Gantt chart, plotting the task bars against a calendar timeline. Here is a table for one of the deliverables from the chart above:

Deliverable / Task	Before / after launch date	Cycle time	Start date	End date
DATASHEET	one week before	6 weeks	12/1	1/15
Source content		1 week	12/1	12/8
Write draft		3 weeks	12/9	12/30
Illustrations		3 weeks	12/9	12/30
Edit and review		1 week	12/31	1/7
Print		1 week	1/8	1/15

Table 16.3 Deliverable planning chart

This table does not take into account weekends or holidays, but they should be considered in a real situation. This table is a quick way to visualize the dates when handoffs need to occur between the team members. This exercise should be repeated for each deliverable. Once the task dates are calculated, then they can be added to the resource allocation table in order to show the overlaps, as in the following example:

Deliverables/ People	Datasheet	White Paper	Sales tool CD
Product Manager- Eric Smith	Outline, provide content 12/1-12/8	Review 1/16	Develop content 1/17-1/24
Contract writer- Miriam Hammer	Write 12/9-12/30	Write 12/15-1/15	Write text content
Corporate editor- Sally Horvath	Edit 12/31-1/17	Edit 1/16-1/23	Edit text content 2/8-2/15
Graphic designer- Amy Pixel	Develop illustrations 12/9-12/30	Develop illustrations 12/15-1/15	Develop artwork 1/24-2/7
Printer- Wordsmith Printing	Print 1/8-1/15	Print 1/24-1/31	
Multimedia producer- LiveArts			Record and edit CD 1/25-2/7

Table 16.4 Resource Allocation with Dates

It is now a simple matter to identify the task overlaps for each team member. Miriam is going to be very busy, and she had does, you will probably need to arrange for an additional writer.

There is also a similar situation with the graphic designer, Amy, but there may be a way to prioritize the work to meet deadlines.

Developing a detailed schedule may seem like a daunting task. However, it will save a tremendous amount of time and frustration later on in the launch, especially when there are several marketing programs going on at one time. The master schedule will clearly indicate peak times when several tasks will occur in parallel, enabling the launch manager to plan resources more effectively. The master schedule will also show dependencies, where one task cannot begin until someone else completes his or her task. The presence of several dependencies involving one person can create a bottleneck in the process. By knowing this ahead of time, the launch manager can reallocate resources to remove the bottleneck. To do this, you will need to arrange the information in a spreadsheet; Microsoft Excel works well for this purpose.

List the deliverable first with a brief description. Each deliverable has a column for the owner, which is the person responsible for producing it. Also add a column for the person who will review the item and approve it for final release. Add a start date, a deadline date, a 'completed' date, and the last column is the status. You now have a launch schedule that you can update weekly to show progress against each deliverable.

The master schedule also becomes a baseline, and can be used to plan workarounds to the schedule when unforeseen events affect the deliverables or the schedule. Most scheduling or project management software enables "what-if" analyses, whereby you can change start and end dates of tasks in order to define the impact on the rest of the schedule.

17

The Launch Budget

Now that you have all of the launch deliverables identified and the schedule completed, the budget needs to be prepared. At the beginning of the launch planning phase, you obtained the total budget for the launch. That number may be a "not-to-exceed" total, or the budget may be divided by type of marketing program, such as a specified amount for marketing materials, PR, advertising, etcetera. You will need to have those numbers handy when you prepare the detailed launch budget.

Launch budgets can be prepared top-down or bottom-up. The top-down method is to allocate an amount for deliverable and then only do as much work on the deliverable as the budget allows. The bottom-up method, also sometimes referred to as "zero-based budgeting", is to estimate the actual production costs for each deliverable, and then allocate the total budget accordingly. This sometimes results in a situation where you can't afford to produce all of the deliverables and therefore have to prioritize. Sometimes you can also end up with some unallocated money, but that can be held in a discretionary line item for emergencies or other opportunities. It's much easier to use the bottom-up approach for launch budgets because it's not possible to produce just a partial deliverable, and it forces prioritization of the deliverables.

Estimating launch budget by deliverable

When you did the resource allocation, each deliverable had an amount of time associated with it, and also possibly some outside costs for writing, design or printing services. For each deliverable, make a list of what it would cost to do in the next two months. That means that if you need to get current bids from outside vendors, you should find out the current cost and not just estimate it from a previous launch, especially if the last launch was several months ago. Here is an example for a brochure:

Brochure:
Writing (internal cost): 40 hours ($1000)
Graphic Designer: $1500
Printing: $2.00 each x 250 copies = $500
TOTAL: $3000

If you have more than one brochure or datasheet that you will be producing for the launch, make sure that you use the appropriate multiplier so that you have the totals for that item. Estimate the cost of all deliverables and enter the total cost by deliverable into a spreadsheet. Add up the total for all deliverables. This is your bottom-up budget for the launch. Figure 17.1 is an example:

Deliverable	$$$
Brochure	3000
Trade shows	2000
White papers	5000
Demo CD	4000
TOTAL	14,000

Figure 17.1 Bottom-up Launch Budget

Second pass: top-down comparison

Compare the total available launch budget with your bottom-up budget. If the available budget is a lower number, you will have to do some prioritization of the items. There are many ways to accomplish this. If you had planned to do multiple brochures or datasheets, you can instead consolidate them into one. That saves writing, design and printing costs. You could also print fewer copies and reserve those copies only for qualified leads or existing customers. In the area of public relations, you can do fewer press releases and send them out less frequently. If press or analyst tours are planned, you may be able to do the tour by teleconference or webcast instead to save on travel expenses. For most marketing materials, you can deliver them on the web instead of in hard copy, which also saves money.

If the available budget is a higher number, you will have the luxury of adding some deliverables, doing more outsourcing or keeping the extra money in a discretionary fund to cover unexpected expenses as the launch is implemented. Sometimes opportunities arise for additional events such as tradeshows, so extra funds could be used for an exhibit. There may also be opportunities to do advertising. Here is an example of an adjusted budget with discretionary funding shown:

Item	Original	Actual	Discretionary
Trade shows	6000	2000	4000
Printed materials	12,000	8000	4000
CD Production	15,000	4000	11,000

Figure 17.2 Adjusted Budget with Discretionary Funds

The final step is to take the adjusted totals for each deliverable and then plot the expenditures by month. You'll want to have your detailed launch schedule handy for this because it will give you the deadlines for when each deliverable will be produced, and therefore when you will have to pay those expenses. Figure 17.3 shows the monthly launch budget:

Item	Jan	Feb	Mar	Apr	May	Jun
Brochure			3000			
Trade show materials			1000		1000	
White paper 1	2500					
White paper 2						2500
Demo CD		4000				

Figure 17.3 Budget by Month

Sometimes as launches proceed through implementation, decisions are made regarding deliverables, or other expenses come up. By having a monthly budget as a baseline, it serves a tool for doing what-if analyses or re-allocating the budget.

18

Compiling the Launch Plan

Developing the launch plan in this sequence, from the deliverables to the people to the schedule to the budget, will help you to identify the resource gaps and will help you to visualize how the work will flow from start to finish. When all tasks and deliverables are plotted in this manner, you will be able to identify the peak periods of activity and will easily be able to see how many tasks will be happening in parallel. From this baseline, you will also be able to report status and to manage the ongoing events during the implementation of the launch. You will also be in a better position to manage the launch budget and make adjustments along the way.

Now that you have all the major pieces of the launch plan developed, it's time to compile all of the elements in a document that you can use to manage the launch. In assembling the resources, schedule and budget, you used some source material and created some high-level elements of the plan. These shouldn't be discarded; they should remain in the launch plan as a reference for people who will be reading and referring to the plan. You also have some detailed elements that you created during the planning process. Figure 18.1 is a diagram of the elements that you will have on hand at this point of the process:

High-level elements for reference:	Detailed elements for managing:
- One-page launch timeline - Deliverables list - Top-level budget	- Launch schedule by month, with key dates - Resource allocation by deliverable - Launch budget by deliverable - Launch budget by month - Launch status sheet for weekly updating

Figure 18.1 Elements of the Launch Plan

Gather all of these documents together, and make sure that each of the documents has a date stamp or version number as to when they were created. In some cases, you may have additional versions of the schedule or budget that you did for a what-if analysis. Those should be part of the plan as well because at some point you may have to use these documents instead of the baseline plan.

Outline for the launch plan

The following outline is an efficient way to organize the information. You may want to keep a printed copy in a 3-ring binder, with tabs for "main plan", "resource list", "schedule" and "budget". That comes in handy in case you need to answer a question quickly while on the phone or in a meeting. As launch manager, you will have a lot of activities going on during any given day, and it will be impossible to memorize the deadlines and budgets for every single deliverable. The launch plan should be used as a ready reference to guide everyday activities for the launch. Keep it near your copy of the marketing plan, which contains the key messages, strategy and other details.

-Title page: Name of Product Being Launched, Launch Date
-Product description from marketing plan
-Launch team members: names and contact information (phone numbers and email addresses), areas of responsibility

High-level Elements:
-Deliverables list from the marketing plan
-One-page launch timeline
-Top-level budget

Elements for Managing:
-Resource allocation by deliverable
-Launch budget by deliverable
-Launch budget by month
-Launch schedule by month
-Launch schedule for weekly status updating

Tracking and Reporting:
-Copies of past weekly status reports
-Schedule of launch meetings
-Minutes of launch meetings

Each member of the launch team should have a partial launch plan that includes the deliverables list and all schedules. Only the launch manager will need the elements that pertain to budgets and resource allocations. All members of the launch team should receive copies of minutes from launch meetings if they are recorded.

Leveraging the plan

As the launch plan is used throughout the launch implementation phase, it becomes a historical record as to how the launch was carried out. It can then be used as a guideline for planning future launches and to analyze for lessons learned so that the process can be improved.

19

Launch Implementation

This chapter is for the launch manager, who must make sense of all the chaos that will occur during the launch implementation. Up to this point in the book, there has been a lot of material presented on how to organize and plan a product launch. When you begin the task of managing the launch implementation, the process ceases to be neat and orderly. There are a million things to be done in too short an amount of time, by people who don't normally work together and who sometimes dislike each other. Even if there is some sort of formal launch process in place that documents what people need to do during the launch implementation phase, people generally have not been trained in the process, or they choose to ignore it and make up their own rules. Managing a launch is very messy and frustrating. Sometimes, the best you can hope for is that people will still speak to you when it's over. However, there are a few things you can do to make your job a little easier.

At the beginning of the implementation phase, you need to set expectations for the launch team. You will need to explain each team member's role and responsibility, as well as the process by which the work will be done. Once the implementation begins, you need to develop the team's working routine in terms of decision-making and consensus. Any conflicts that arise must be resolved quickly. Flexibility is critical for completing the work tasks; the plan must be adaptable, in order to accommodate unforeseen change. Open and frequent communication with the launch team is necessary to keep everyone moving forward. It's also important to motivate the team by recognizing and celebrating accomplishments throughout the implementation phase.

Getting started

As a launch manager, you will need to establish a reporting path as well as an escalation path to your management before the launch begins. You may occasionally need your manager's help in order to raise issues that need to be decided by senior management, to help obtain additional resources that you need on the team, and to help resolve conflicts. Your manager will also most likely require periodic reporting of progress on the launch implementation.

Starting a launch implementation is a little bit like installing and using new software. You need to familiarize yourself with what is in the software application, what the software does, and how to make it work. You need to do the same thing with a launch team as you begin the work. With your launch plan in hand, and the team in place, it's time to get started.

The first task is to set up a launch kickoff meeting. Members of the launch team need to attend this meeting, and you may also want to invite other managers or people who may be peripherally involved in the launch. Those who cannot attend in person should participate via teleconferencing or web conferencing. At the kickoff meeting, every person on the launch team should be given a copy of the marketing plan and the launch plan, to use as reference material during the implementation phase. The purpose of the kickoff meeting is to set expectations for the launch implementation and to explain the roles and responsibilities of the people on the launch team.

Another purpose of the kickoff meeting is to educate people about the implementation process. Quite often, launch team members have never been on a launch team before, and they don't know what work needs to be done by the team. In most cases, the work that people do on a launch team is not the same as the work they do in their regular jobs. For that reason, you need to explain what the team will be doing and who will be doing it. The tasks, along with their assigned owners, are identified in the launch plan. People may have some idea of how to do an individual task, but they may not know how to handle tasks in parallel, or how one task affects another. People need to be educated about how the work will be done as a team, how to identify problems and issues, what will happen during launch meetings, and how the group will be monitored.

Sometimes there is an existing implementation process that has been used for previous product launches. You may want to use it for your launch implementation. However, if it ceases to work for the team, then change it. You shouldn't follow process merely for the sake of process, if doing so will interfere with meeting the schedule and goals for the launch. In one company, a launch process was finally developed by the marketing department after several launch failures and much "finger-pointing". The final process report was elegant. Every department involved in launch and their interfaces were thoroughly described for every possible launch activity. Cycle times were estimated in detail, to the nearest half-day. Outlines of all launch documents were provided, along with examples. The launch process document, when completed, was more than 50 pages long. What happened to it? Not many people read it; it was too long. The engineering and product development organizations refused to follow it because they had not been consulted or asked for their input when the process was being written. An effective business process is a tool that should work for all of the company, and not just one department. If it doesn't, the process should be modified until it does work. Every organization, both internal and external, that is involved in product launch needs to be involved in creating the process. If that can be accomplished, then people are generally more willing to follow a process that they have had a part in creating.

Sometimes, outside vendors or contractors are used during the launch phase to provide deliverables related to the launch. These individuals need to also participate in the launch team meetings. Often, these outside vendors will need background material about the product or special briefings, so that they can understand more about the product that is being launched. You should provide them with copies of the marketing plan and launch plan, and arrange any special meetings that may be required to educate them before the launch kickoff meeting.

Maintaining momentum

After the kickoff meeting, the team should have a pretty good idea of the work that needs to be done. They also should know who is doing which tasks, and what will happen during the launch team meetings. The launch team members can now adjust their calendars to accommodate all of the commitments they have made to do the work during the implementation phase. All the outside vendors are ready to go, and you have arranged a reporting path to your manager. The work can now begin.

To maintain the momentum during the launch implementation launch meetings need to be held regularly with the team. At a minimum, these should take place weekly throughout the implementation. Launch meetings provide a forum for checking status of launch deliverables, resolving issues, making decisions, and keeping everyone informed. During each launch meeting, members should report progress on tasks, identify areas where they need help, and participate in any group discussions that take place to accommodate changes in the plan or to make decisions. Launch meetings generally last from one to two hours.

During the implementation, disputes often arise between marketing and product development regarding decision-making. For instance, a central marketing group may believe they have the charter and the responsibility to decide what is best for product development. The product manager may believe that the marketing group only exists to serve him or her. It is the responsibility of the launch manager to arbitrate these disputes. The important thing is to defuse these situations as soon as possible; don't let them fester. If you cannot resolve the dispute yourself, escalate the problem to your manager as soon as possible so that the team can move forward. A dispute can hamper the momentum of the whole team, even for the team members who are not directly involved in the dispute. Harmony is important so that the team can remain focused on the task at hand: getting through the implementation.

Because the launch team is a cross-functional team, you need to operate by consensus if possible. It is important that the team members representing different organizations in the company have an opportunity to contribute ideas during brainstorming, and that they have input to decisions made by the team. However, you don't want to go overboard with consensus if the team is stalled or at an impasse. If that happens, be prepared to make a decision that will be in the best interest of the launch objectives, and then move on. You won't make friends, but it is more important to keep the team moving forward.

Dealing with change

The best laid plans of mice and launch managers often go awry. During the launch implementation, you should expect that one or more events will disrupt your carefully prepared launch plan. You need to flexible, and the plan needs to be flexible.

One of the more common types of disruption is a change in the competitive landscape, such as a new competing product being announced, or company management implementing a new strategic direction for the company. In one launch implementation, a competitor's new product was announced the week before the company's scheduled press release. The press release date and the press tour was delayed one week to give the company time to adjust the positioning and messages in order to be able to respond to the questions that the press would undoubtedly ask. Changing those two dates had quite a ripple effect in all of the deliverables that were tied to the date of the press release. All of the content in the sales collateral and training materials had to be changed accordingly. Consequently, the sales team received the new material much later than they should have. However, the product positioning in this particular case was absolutely critical because it was an entry into a new vertical market. Without repositioning, the product would not have received the attention it needed. Sometimes, the schedule has to be sacrificed in order to meet the ultimate marketing objective.

In another example, a company decided to announce a major reorganization one week before a major new product was to be announced. The company was reorganizing by market segment, in order to better compete in their overall market. All of the product development organizations were shifted so that they would have a market focus instead of a technology focus. As a consequence, all of the collateral had to be changed to reflect the new positioning. The technical descriptions of the product had to be rewritten from a technology focus to a market focus. All of the collateral and other marketing deliverables were delayed by one month to accommodate the changes. However, rewriting and retargeting the marketing materials helped reinforce the company's new focus on the markets. The benefits of reinforcing the larger corporate message in this case far outweighed the cost of reworking the marketing materials.

Changes like these have a huge impact on the momentum of the launch team, and these events can be de-motivating. However, you shouldn't feel obligated to solve the problem yourself; you have a launch team to help you. The best thing to do is to lead the team in coming up with a solution together, encouraging everyone to brainstorm and devise a new plan.

Communication

Effective communication is vital to the launch process and helps keep the team focused on the ultimate launch goals. Frequent communication also keeps people involved and motivated so that the implementation continues to move forward.

Regular meetings are necessary to assess status of deliverables, deal with changes to the implementation plan if necessary, and facilitate group decision-making. Other types of communications such as email or voicemail should also be used to remind people of action items and upcoming events, distribute agendas, and report status.

There are many books about how to run effective meetings. Some of these techniques work well for launch meetings. Agendas should be developed for each meeting and sent out ahead of time to meeting participants. Action items that are assigned during the meeting should be recorded in a master log, noting the owner of the action item, the date assigned, the date due, and description of the action. Detailed minutes of the meeting should be distributed no more than one day after the launch meeting. The meeting time should be structured so that the agenda is followed, allowing time for reporting of status and any discussions that are necessary to resolve issues. The meeting should begin and end on time. Any rambling discussions should be interrupted and "taken off-line" if they don't provide value to the team as a whole.

Setting up a centralized launch center

During the chaos of launch, it is challenging to communicate with the many people involved with various aspects of launch. The marketing people need to communicate with the technical people and the sales training people and the public relations people and the lucky launch manager needs to keep all the information updated and distributed. To make life easier, I recommend to my clients that they set up a dedicated area on a private, internal network that can function as "launch central", and appoint someone from the launch team as the keeper of the information that resides there.

A Repository and Hub

The online launch center should contain all of the information about all the company's launches: the what, when, where and who. It should be the centralized repository where the latest and most up to date information about each launch can be found. Launch information stored here should include high-level information such as the company's product roadmap, the schedule of launches for the year, and strategic objectives for each launch. There should also be a set of files for each major launch planned that includes a detailed launch timeline, any documents that reflect pre-development market requirements, competitive analysis information, specs for the product, information on the beta customer program, a list of all launch deliverables, and a schedule of launch team meetings and key dates for events.

The launch center should act as a hub for communicating with all key individuals involved in the launch, and employees who need launch information. Additionally, the launch center can store the working copies of marketing materials such as brochures, datasheets and sales presentations, so that individuals can collaboratively develop, review and revise these documents online.

Access

Who should be able to access the information in the launch center? Certainly every member of the launch team and those providing key input for the launch. Sometimes, these key people are not employees, such as external vendors or contractors. These individuals may need password-controlled access to the company's network.

Sometimes any employee can have access to the launch center, at least as far as reading files; they might not be able to revise or change files that reside there, however. Some companies want to make the information available company-wide, and others worry that company-confidential information could fall into the wrong hands either inadvertently or on purpose. Company policy will determine how access should be controlled. In any case, all internal launch documents should be clearly marked as company confidential.

Updates

Someone from the launch team should be designated to post and update the information in the launch center, controlled by passwords. It's important to show revision dates, and to notify key members of the launch team by email that the files have been updated. Use of automated date and time stamps can help control versions of documents.

It's also critical to update launch documents in the center as quickly as the changes are made, especially if there are any changes to the launch schedule or timeline. There are so many organizations that interact for launch that the slightest change will ripple through the whole system. Keeping the information current will also help increase use of the center - if people know that there's somewhere they can go to get the latest information about the launch, they will begin to rely on it.

Organizing the Content

The information in the launch center should be organized in a hierarchical fashion. At the top level, there should be either a list or diagram that shows the product roadmap for the year, along with a timeline of launches by month for the entire year. This information usually comes from strategic planning documents that are revised at the beginning of a year or a business cycle, and links to the original documents can be placed in this section. These might be strategic plans or the CEO's last PowerPoint presentation to the employees. In addition to the plan for the future, sometimes companies will post a list of the products already available in the company in this section of the launch center.

Each product or service to be launched should have its own section in the launch center; this may be a folder with many files in it. For each launch, here is a checklist of information that might be useful for the launch. Not everyone will include all of these files because they want to keep things simple, so you can choose whatever is needed most by the launch team and company:

-Launch team members and contact information
-Schedule of launch team meetings
-Detailed launch timeline
-List of launch deliverables and key deadlines, responsible individuals
-Marketing materials in progress (working copies)

-Detailed product description and relationship to product families
-Development schedule, including beta testing
-Target customer description and value proposition
-General market overview and key trends
-Competitive Overview
-Competitive analysis of companies
-Competitive analysis by product
-Key differentiators
-Market strategy
-Positioning against key competitors
-Key messages – corporate and product level
-Distribution channels

-Sales team information:
-Key customer accounts, targeted new customers
-Customer presentations
-Collateral and marketing materials available
-Schedule of key trade shows and events

-Key web links to other documents, presentations, and planning documents

Getting People to Use It

It's one thing to set up such a center; it's quite another to get people to use it. The first hurdle is making sure people are aware that there is one. This can be accomplished using an internal email broadcast, or better yet, a personal presentation by the launch manager for each of the key functional groups involved in launch.

Sometimes it takes pressure from senior management to encourage employees to use the center, so it's a good idea to line up some support before the center is created. Employees are more likely to pay attention if the directive comes from the top.

Another way to encourage use is to make the online launch center as easy to use as possible. If users report errors or crashes, make sure that they are fixed as soon as possible. Also, be willing to take action on any suggestions for improvement that you receive from users. After all, the whole purpose of having a center is to make launches easier for everyone involved.

Motivation

Everyone on the launch team faces great pressure to meet deadlines. A certain amount of procrastination or work overload occurs for all team members during this time, and it is especially challenging for the launch manager to motivate the team and keep them moving forward. Because of the time pressure, meetings should be run not only so that they begin and end on time, but also so they respect people's deadlines. If it's more important that team members spend time completing a launch task than attending a weekly launch meeting, then encourage them to do so.

Virtual teams are difficult to manage because of the short duration of the launch, and also because there isn't a distinct reporting hierarchy. It helps to encourage group discussion and
participation so that people can get to know each other and
develop a team-oriented work style. People need to feel that
they are valued and respected contributors to the team. As the
launch manager, you need to facilitate open discussion and encourage all team members to join in by asking their opinion or
advice.

Email messages thanking people for outstanding efforts help
tremendously. They only take a few minutes to write, but they
go a long way toward keeping people motivated. Even if it's a
small accomplishment from a very long list of things to do,
send a brief thank you, with a copy to the person's manager.
People like to be recognized.

When the team meets critical milestones, take the time to celebrate! You can have refreshments brought in, or you can purchase small commemorative gifts to hand out to people. This
type of event helps reinforce the team spirit, but is also a reward for hard work.

Whenever possible, use humor to lighten up the pressure of
deadlines and chaos. Collect little cartoons or one-liners that
are appropriate to the situation and distribute them in launch
meetings. Encourage people to share jokes and humorous experiences. And don't be afraid to laugh at yourselves. Life is
too short to be so serious.

Going Forward

20

Launch Process Improvement

Everyone is usually relieved when the launch is finally over. After the launch date, there may be one or two additional launch meetings held to wrap up all the activities. The launch manager should dedicate one meeting to discussing the lessons learned from the launch and how the launch process may be improved the next time. Many things can go wrong during product launches. How the launch team handles these issues and changes needs to be captured and documented, so that future launch teams can improve future product launches.

New product launches are the lifeblood of most high technology companies. Some companies set up a separate organization to manage all product launches for the company. Anything that can be done to improve the process of launching products should be seriously considered and if possible, implemented. If you have had outside consultants or vendors helping to manage the launch, ask them to make recommendations as to how to improve the process.

Sometimes the experience of serving on a product launch team can have a positive impact on how the launch team members deal with new products when they return to their respective organizations. In effect, they can transfer that learning and perspective to their own organizations, to instill a greater awareness about the importance of new products. Over time, that phenomenon helps to align the company toward meeting its strategic goals, and can lead to sustainable long-term growth.

After the launch

Post-launch activities may include wrapping up any marketing programs that didn't need to be completed by the announcement date, posting information to intranet sites, supplying marketing materials to trade shows, and fulfillment for brochures or other marketing materials that will be distributed via direct mail. The team may be required to meet for one or two sessions after the launch date in order to complete all of the deliverables. These post-launch meetings are an excellent forum for sharing feedback regarding the press release and associated press coverage. It may also be a good time to celebrate another major milestone for the team.

Lessons Learned

At least one of the post-launch meetings should be dedicated to discussing what went right and what went wrong during the launch implementation. Open and candid discussion should be conducted to identify gaps in the process, roles and responsibilities, and decision-making. Sometimes there are disputes between organizations as to who 'owns' each launch deliverable or who gets to make the decisions; seek recommendations on changes to the process. Ask for input on the positive things as well as the negative. Minutes of these "lessons learned" sessions should be written up into a lessons learned report and distributed to the whole launch team, giving them an opportunity to review what was said in the meeting as well as to contribute more feedback.

Many things can go wrong during a launch implementation, and people have many war stories that hold valuable lessons for planning future launches. Some common war stories include: vaporware (features and functions of the product do not exist); surprise press releases (sales force finds out about the company's new product from a customer); and competitive end-run (competitor announces their product the day before your press release). Launches don't always go as planned. What's important is to document how the launch team responded to the changed conditions.

Let's look at one of the potential snags, the competitive end-run, and how a launch team might handle it. Competitive moves can happen at any time. When they happen right before you are about to announce your product, there are many ways to turn this threat into an opportunity. You can analyze what your competitor has announced, and reposition your product more strongly by revising the messaging in the press release. It may be too late to do that for any collateral that's already been created, but you can certainly warn your sales force about this. You can also create some bulletin for your indirect channels, so that they will have their questions answered regarding how your product compares to the competitor's new offering. It gives you an opportunity to create leverage with your channels. If the product announced by your competitor is very similar to yours, this should be regarded as market validation for your product. The trick is to leverage your announcement and post-launch marketing programs so that your product is properly and clearly differentiated. In one case where this situation actually occurred, the team updated the sales force immediately, and repackaged the messages from the press tour such that the competitor's product validated the market for the company's product. That strategy worked very well. This was also a helpful insight for the next launch team; they were more careful about monitoring the competitors.

Dealing with late marketing deliverables is also another common "war story". Sometimes, late deliverables can't be avoided, especially if many different pieces of collateral have deadlines for the same day as the announcement. One company in this situation re-prioritized the collateral two weeks before the launch date, and completed only the most crucial pieces that were needed for the press kit and for the sales force. Getting temporary information out to the sales force and to channel partners over the web also proved to be a quick way to reach them before print versions could be completed and distributed. Creating shorter versions of collateral that contained copy but not final layout or graphics was another compromise. The launch team spent the time they had to create a solid set of questions and answers instead; this enabled the sales force and the press tour participants to speak intelligently about the product even though the nice glossy brochure wasn't quite ready.

The lessons learned report from each launch should be used to make modifications to the launch process. In one company, the lessons learned report revealed an issue with assigning product managers to launch teams. In the course of a three-month launch, there were three different product managers assigned from the development group. This created a lack of consistency and a need to re-educate the different product managers each time a new one joined the team. The company made a change to the process requiring that only one product manager be assigned, one who could commit to supporting the launch team for the duration of the launch.

When everyone has had a chance to provide input to the lessons learned discussion, take the time to compile it in a formalized document and then send it to marketing, product development, the launch team, and senior management. The report should contain recommendations on any company policies and procedures that might need changing, as well as the steps that need to be taken to improve the launch process.

Process engineering

If there is no formal launch process in place in your organization, it's a good idea to start outlining and documenting a process, so that it can be used for future launches in the company. Sometimes, this becomes a trial and error effort, evaluating things that worked versus things that didn't work as you go through each launch. Every launch will be a little bit different, but it should still be possible to find some common process elements that can act as a guide for the next launch team. To document a process, you need to describe the flow of information and documents among different functional organizations, and the order in which the actions occur. Use simple flow charts to show the handoff from one organization to another. With each launch that is implemented, you can fine-tune the process until it represents the most effective set of actions, participants and handoffs.

Once the process is developed, then it is advisable to make the document available company-wide. This can easily be accomplished through the company intranet or by email. Even if people are not currently assigned to a launch team, having this document available helps tremendously in the early stages of staffing for the next launch. Some companies even give internal presentations to employees about product launches. If you are in a small company, it's still a good idea to document the process and let everyone know how the launch will work.

Planning future launches

At NASA headquarters, during the heyday of the Space Shuttle missions, there was a room that was reserved for the Shuttle manifest. This manifest was a magnetic board that stretched from floor to ceiling. For each Shuttle mission, there was a series of magnets in various shapes representing the various payloads, experiments, astronauts, and mission specialists. Each series of magnets was arranged in a horizontal row. The top row of magnets represented the current year's missions, and vertically below were additional rows representing ten years into the future. It was like a giant Gantt chart, and NASA managers used it to plan and re-plan missions as budgets changed, as technology advanced, and as launches had to be rescheduled. When one mission was rescheduled, it affected one or more future missions.

In a company, it is just as important to have a launch roadmap that is planned out at least two years, and that is fully integrated with the company's strategic planning and objectives. A separate room need not be built for this purpose; a simple Gantt chart will work just fine. Future product launches should be plotted on the chart so that the launch teams can be trained, assembled, and assigned to launch projects. Without such a roadmap, it will be next to impossible to manage several launches at one time.

Growing a launch organization

As a company does successive product launches and develops a repeatable launch process, setting up a dedicated launch organization to focus solely on product launch implementation may make sense. The organization would include multifunctional representatives from different departments within the company, and only the product manager would be different each time. For consistency and speed, this approach is a good one, if the organization can spare the resources to do it.

If the decision is made to set up a launch organization, a standardized launch process should be set up and followed with each launch. The lessons learned from each launch should still be used, however, to improve and enhance the process.

Postscript

Launches will always be an important part of managing and operating high tech companies. The investment in time and money to develop effective techniques for planning and implementing product launches will provide returns directly to the bottom line many years into the future.

Index

A

Acquisitions, as strategic
   objective 44-45
Advertising 159, 168-172

B

Beta tests 29, 35
Branding 43, 169
Brochures 150
Budgets 2, 19, 142-143,
   169, 171, 201, 203,
   223-226, 228
Business model(s) 95-97

C

Channels
   direct 98, 100-102, 106
   indirect 98, 102-106,
      122, 180-181
Collateral
   definition 141
   electronic 141, 151-152
   print 141, 148-151

Communication
   among launch team
      members 232, 237-238
   among all employees
      179-180
Competition
   analysis of 46, 77-93
Competitive environment
   79-80
Competitive matrix 89-91
Cross-functional involve-
   ment in launch 2, 6,
   13, 22, 29, 205-208,
   235
Customer
   buying behavior 16, 17,
      51-57
   definition 51-64, 69
   problem 58-60, 72, 131
   value proposition 60-61,
      69
Customer support 36, 177-
   179, 206

Also by Catherine Kitcho:

From Idea to Launch at Internet Speed

This is a complete guide to new product management for today's dynamic economy...from initial concept to market launch. It includes the latest new product management strategies and techniques to reach your market faster and to reap greater profit. Based on interviews with 20 executives from a wide variety of companies and Catherine Kitcho's decades of experience in managing new products, *From Idea to Launch at Internet Speed* represents an impressive collection of knowledge and practices, all with an emphasis on profitability. Anyone who is focused on managing new products will find this book valuable, including CEOs, new business executives, product managers, and entrepreneurs.

ISBN 1-929936-00-1
Hardcover, 361 pages, with accompanying CD.

Visit our website at **www.pelepubs.com** for ordering information, current price, and availability.

Or, call toll-free: 1-877-PELEPUBS

PELE

P U B L I C A T I O N S

LEGENDARY LOCALS

——— OF ———

NEWBURYPORT

MASSACHUSETTS

Newburyport Harbor
During the mid- to late 1800s, Newburyport Harbor served as berth for the magnificent clipper ships built by master shipbuilder and legendary local Donald McKay (page 64). Today, sailboats, fishing vessels, whale watching boats, and other types of watercraft find berth in the harbor. (Courtesy of the author.)

Page 1: Harry O'Connor
Harry O'Connor, Plum Island resident and founder of the "World's Shortest St. Patrick's Day Parade" is pictured here and on page 31. (Courtesy of Charlotte Vincent.)

Legendary Locals is an imprint of Arcadia Publishing
Charleston, South Carolina

Printed in the United States of America

Library of Congress Control Number: 2013952069

For all general information, please contact Arcadia Publishing:
Telephone 843-853-2070
Fax 843-853-0044
E-mail sales@arcadiapublishing.com
For customer service and orders:
Toll-Free 1-888-313-2665

Visit us on the Internet at www.arcadiapublishing.com

Dedication
This book is dedicated to the colorful citizens of Newburyport, past and present, who have left their imprint upon the city.

ON THE FRONT COVER: Clockwise from top left: Richard Simkins, owner of the Grog (Courtesy of the author; see page 74), 1st Lt. Derek Hines (Courtesy of the Hines family; see page 10), Bethany Groff, North Shore regional manager for Historic New England (Courtesy of the author; see page 93), Frank G. Cousins Jr., sheriff of Essex County (Courtesy of the author; see page 21), Peter G. Kelly, owner of Kelly's True Value Hardware (Courtesy of the author; see page 62), Mickey, feral cat mascot for the Merrimack River Feline Rescue Society (Courtesy of Richard Boisvert; see page 18), Danny Harrington, saxophone player (Courtesy of the author; see page 112), William Lloyd Garrison, national abolitionist (Photograph by author, courtesy of Brown Square; see page 38), Ariele Ebacher, wire walker (Photograph by Jim Newberry, courtesy of Ariele Ebacher; see page 118).

ON THE BACK COVER: From left to right: William G. Taplin, also known as "Captain Bill," of the *Yankee Clipper* (Courtesy of the author; see page 58), Sue Little, owner of Jabberwocky Bookshop (Courtesy of the author; see page 70).

CONTENTS

ACKNOWLEDGMENTS

I would like to extend special thanks to Newburyport historians and authors Ghlee E. Woodworth, Jean Foley Doyle, Bethany Groff, and Marge and Skip Motes. I give special thanks also to Jessica Gill, archivist at the Newburyport Public Library, and to Jay S. Williamson, curator for the Historical Society of Old Newbury, for their help with past legendary locals.

Thank you to Beth Welch, granddaughter of writer J.P. Marquand; Pam Britton, mother to community builder PJ Britton; Frank LaBarba, son of the legendary Nicola "Nick" of Nick's Pizza; Ruth Landreth, mother to Travis, Susannah, and Molly Landreth, and Mary Ann Lawler, daughter to Mayor George H. Lawler Jr. and granddaughter to police officer George H. Lawler Sr. Each of these individuals took a family portrait from their wall at home or from their place of business so that I could borrow and scan the image for inclusion in this book.

Patricia Connelly, Daphine Neville, Jan and John DeWitt, and Christopher Paglia provided sound input and guidance. Christopher Paglia also provided technical support, and Tina Lambert provided production support. I am grateful to them all.

Unless otherwise noted, all photographs are courtesy of the author.

First Religious Society
This is the steeple at First Religious Society at the Unitarian Universalist Church. (Courtesy of Edith Heyck.)

INTRODUCTION

Situated on the banks of the Merrimack River, the historic seaport of Newburyport, Massachusetts, has been—and continues to be—home to a colorful citizenry, which includes shipbuilders, sea captains, patriots, activists, artists, writers, musicians, actors, brewers, and eccentrics.

The year 2014 marks the 250th anniversary of Newburyport becoming its own town; prior to 1764, Newburyport had been part of neighboring Newbury. In 1851, Newburyport became a city.

Celebrated as the birthplace of the United States Coast Guard and rich in maritime history, Newburyport earned the nickname "Clipper City" for the fast-sailing vessels crafted by its prominent shipbuilders and sailed across the seas by its legendary sea captains. Today's residents call their city simply "the Port."

Some townies might call out to one another with the friendly greeting, "Yeat!" As the story goes, the nonsensical Newburyport-centric term was once used by Newburyport enlisted military personnel deployed overseas to identify fellow Newburyporters. Calling out "Yeat!" and receiving a like response would unite the fellow townies. The versatile idiom has also served as a benign curse word. Today, "Yeat!" is an emblem of a local brewer, etched upon the lid of each beer can.

Before breweries and beer, there were distilleries and rum. In the late 1700s, an affluent merchant whose wealth grew with his investments in sugar and molasses erected a rum distillery on Newburyport's waterfront. He also established a small city park where he built a private residence that later served as a boardinghouse before becoming a hotel. Today, the stately brick building is named after one of the country's most prominent abolitionists and a Newburyport native son. Exercising his right to the freedom of speech, this fiery abolitionist, who died in 1879, spoke out against slavery and used the press to spread his message of equal rights for all.

More than 80 years after Garrison's death, an unassuming Newburyport minister of steadfast integrity and fierce dedication to humanity invited an expert on extremism to speak to his congregation. The event became a touchstone of passion for locals when the founder of the American Nazi Party almost crashed it. Now retired, the minister's legacy of open dialog, understanding, respect, and love carries on through the speaker series that his church continues.

Newburyport's wellspring of activism includes everyday citizens and military heroes trying to make a difference in their community and the world. A former Newburyport resident who wanted to pay tribute to those who perished in the country's 9/11 attack and to the enlisted men and women who protect our nation, including those who lost their lives in service, founded the Field of Honor. The patriotic display of American flags is erected each year on the Bartlett Mall.

One Newburyport son who lost his life while serving his country in Afghanistan is lovingly remembered with the annual Flag Day 5K race through Newburyport. The race benefits a soldiers' assistance fund in honor of the fallen hero.

A history of activism is matched by Newburyport's civic pride. Devotion to their city is what led visionary leaders of the 1960s and 1970s—importantly two of the city's mayors—to implement a plan to restore and preserve Newburyport's historic downtown, which had fallen to neglect and disrepair.

Today's merchants proudly maintain pretty storefronts that adorn downtown Newburyport, as do owners of the stores in the nearby Tannery Marketplace. An independent bookstore owner, a purveyor of vinyl records, and an importer of wares from around the world that include jewelry and Indonesian textiles are some of Newburyport's long-established business owners.

Newburyport's business community of yesteryear included a self-titled lord and seafaring trade merchants. The present business community includes a multigenerational pizza shop and a chief executive officer of a worldwide manufacturing company.

A fountainhead for the arts, Newburyport was home to a successful female artist who painted miniature portraits and to a gentleman landscape painter who founded the Newburyport Art Association. Today's artists find inspiration in city landscapes, Plum Island marshes, and even in old trucks. Historic literary bards include a Gothic short-story writer and a Pulitzer Prize recipient. The city's contemporary literati include a Dominican-born, award-winning poet and an award-winning writer from the Emerald Isle. A vibrant theater community has produced acclaimed playwrights, thespians, and even a wire walker. The music community includes funk, blues, soul singers, harmonica-wielding entertainers, a flutist, soft rock and post-punk rockers, jazz drummers, and classical guitarists.

The city's athletes include a marathon runner who completed the historic Athens Classic Marathon in Greece; a married couple who runs to raise funds for a debilitating brain disease; three siblings, one a running phenomenon whose life was too brief and his two sisters who continue to run in his honor; and a nuclear physicist who swam the English Channel.

These individuals and others highlighted in *Legendary Locals of Newburyport* are a sampling of the many interesting individuals who have left their imprint upon this historic seaport.

Firehouse Center for the Arts
The Firehouse Center for the Arts was built as a market house and lyceum in 1823 and served as the Central Fire Station from the mid-1800s until 1980. It then opened as a cultural center in 1991.

CHAPTER ONE

Public Servants

Newburyporters have helped make their city, and the world, a better place to live. Caleb Cushing, who was elected Newburyport's first mayor in 1851, later served as legal advisor to Pres. Abraham Lincoln.

More than a century later, two mayoral visionaries would be credited with helping to save the city's downtown from becoming a strip mall. When a federal document authorizing the demolition of the downtown was placed before Mayor George H. Lawler Jr. in the late 1960s, he refused to sign it. Instead, he reached out to local preservationists to develop a plan that would safeguard Newburyport's history. Mayor Byron J. Matthews, who served the city following Lawler's term, demonstrated strong leadership in guiding the historic preservation plan to realization.

In 1968, a young Newburyport boy, who would one day become the sheriff of Essex County, accompanied his mother to a speaking event outside the city's post office. The speaker was Alabama governor George Wallace, then a presidential candidate known for his segregationist views. Sheriff Frank G. Cousins Jr. recalls learning that day the importance of listening to polar views and the accompanying responsibility of dismantling hatred.

The city of Newburyport wept when hometown boy and 1st Lt. Derek Hines was killed in a firefight in Afghanistan in 2005. The city's annual Flag Day 5K race honors the fallen hero.

Firefighters, teachers, doctors, librarians, and even the feral cat mascot for the Merrimack River Feline Rescue Society are included in this chapter as those whose service has improved the lives of others.

Derek Hines (1980–2005)

The legacy of 1st Lt. Derek Hines is one of selflessness, bravery, and patriotism when he was killed in a firefight in Afghanistan in 2005. The American hero and former star hockey player for West Point is lovingly remembered by his father as the little boy who once fell to the floor while climbing stacks of dog food in the front of Shaw's supermarket. "Derek always seemed to find different ways to cut his head well enough for stitches," Steven Hines said of his oldest child in a touching and emotional eulogy.

Sue Hines, Derek's mother, shares that one of her son's elementary school teachers once described him as "spirited," an understatement, according to his father.

As a big brother, Derek was a role model to his younger brothers, Michael and Trevor, and to his sister, Ashley.

Hines was also an example to his hockey teammates, to his fellow soldiers, to his country, to his Newburyport community, and to humanity.

Considered small for a hockey player, his coach at West Point says that Hines's stature was "outsized in his passion for the game." Hines would bring this outsized passion with him in combat. He once ran through enemy fire to retrieve his squad's mortar. When his Humvee was attacked, Hines climbed atop the vehicle and fired his machine gun at enemy troops. After a bomb exploded near the Humvee, killing his entire squad, Hines pulled each body from the burning vehicle.

Hines was defending his squad when he gave the ultimate sacrifice. He managed to take down a Taliban commander who had disguised himself in traditional garb as an Afghanistan woman and open-fired before Hines lost his own life.

His former commanding officer said in a personal tribute, "Derek lived so that he could touch our lives, however briefly, and make us better people." A bridge over the Merrimack River connecting Newburyport and Amesbury was renamed the Hines Bridge in honor of the local hero.

The annual Flag Day 5K race through Newburyport benefits the 1st Lieutenant Derek Hines Soldiers Assistance Fund. Supporting Massachusetts's soldiers who have suffered serious or life-altering injuries while on active duty, the fund honors the memory of Hines.

"He truly believed in his mission that he was making the world a better place," Steven Hines said in his eulogy to his son. (Courtesy of the Hines family.)

Alex Hasapis (1932–)

"I dreamed of flying since I was a kid," says Alex Hasapis. Although he served in the Air Force during the Korean conflict, he did not get to fly a plane. That changed when he retired from the private sector.

His son-in-law, a commercial pilot with a private airplane, got Hasapis started. "And with the great support from my wife, Charlotte," Hasapis says, "I received my pilot's license at age 64."

He is the first pilot from Plum Island Airport to be inducted into the United Flying Octogenarians, or UFO. Founded to "promote longevity and safety in aviation" and representing "the interest of senior pilots worldwide," inductees must have been a "pilot in command" at or beyond the age of 80.

Hasapis keeps his Varga airplane at Plum Island Airport, where he is the airport's public relations director.

Mayor Andrew J. "Bossy" Gillis (1896–1965)

He was a political pugilist, jailbird, perennial provocateur, and six-term Newburyport mayor. Alternately eviscerated and celebrated by citizens, Bossy Gillis won his first election in 1927 and his last in 1957 with a 14-year hiatus in between his tenure. Gillis's name appear on the ballot in each election until his death on November 4, 1965, shortly after the polls closed on his final, and failed, mayoral bid.

Establishing justice between the city's elite, those who lived in the High Street mansions once occupied by sea captains and the common folk who dwelled in the city's grittier neighborhoods, fueled Gillis's initial mayoral ambition. Or perhaps he wanted to settle a score. After the death of his mother, who raised Gillis after his father abandoned them, Gillis vowed, "I made up my mind I'd make Newburyport eat out of a Gillis hand . . . I wanted to be sitting on top of the town that had called me and my mother riff-raff."

Gillis was a paradox—he ran on an everyman platform and reached out to all the city's ethnicities—yet he seemed to be oblivious to the affront he caused with his lexicon of racial slurs.

His tenure was defined by diatribes, fistfights, and short stints of jail time resulting from his various infractions (which included socking a mayoral predecessor in the jaw). He often governed the city from his filling station in Market Square, which he referred to as "little city hall." Gillis filled the tanks of his constituents with the no-name gas that he sold, undercutting competitors.

Characterized as "paunchy" and "voluble" and as a "red-haired, hot-tempered Irishman" whose actions drew notoriety to himself and to his hometown, Gillis proudly wore his visceral flaws as an authentic human being. Whether he was loathed or loved by those in his community was inconsequential to him. (Below, courtesy of the Newburyport Archival Center at the NPL; inset, courtesy of Newburyport City Hall.)

Thomas H. Howard (1955–)

City Marshal Thomas H. Howard grew up in Newburyport's 1690 Towle House, adjacent to the famed former silver factory of the same name, on the banks of the Merrimack River. One of his boyhood memories is of a dramatic shoot-out between Newburyport police officer George H. Lawler Sr. and robbers who had intercepted the factory workers' weekly payroll delivery.

"I wanted to be a cop from day one," Howard says. That credit goes to his dad, who had been a special details police officer.

Marshal began as a special details officer in neighboring Newbury. He was hired as a police officer for the city of Newburyport in 1978 and rose through the ranks to become city marshal in 2001.

A tenet of Howard's leadership is community-based policing. Through his "park, walk, and talk" initiative, Howard encourages his officers to park and step out of their vehicles, walk through the city's neighborhoods, and talk with the people who live there. "Interacting with the community one-on-one is really great at breaking down barriers," Howard asserts.

Cultivating a rapport with the citizens he serves and protects is of great importance to Howard. He still likes to stroll through the downtown each day. "I like to see what's going on and say hello to people," he says.

Howard jokes that a typical day as city marshal lasts about 18 seconds. But he is not joking when he says that his police department operates 24 hours a day and 7 days a week as a social service organization. "We're more than law enforcement," Howard says. "Oftentimes, we act as a buffer or support system for people."

"At the end of the day," Howard states, "what's important is helping fellow human beings." (Courtesy of Melissa Leary.)

Dorothy "Dottie" LaFrance (1946–)
Newburyport's head librarian Dottie LaFrance, who retired in 2008 with more than 30 years of service, brought a proud stewardship to her role. Preserving and sharing local historical and genealogical treasures she had discovered in the course of inventorying library collections back in 1977 was a personal and professional goal she realized with the 2001 library expansion and renovation.

Today, all these treasures—Newburyport historical resources that include books, documents, photographs, and maps—are housed inside the climate-controlled archival room.

LaFrance considers the decade-long, multimillion-dollar expansion and renovation of the 1771 Tracy Mansion, which housed the original library, a crowning achievement.

"It was important that the library retain its history and also be warm and welcoming," LaFrance says. When the library reopened on May 6, 2001, LaFrance stood on its balcony and watched hundreds of appreciative citizens come through the door.

Built 1771
Newburyport Public Library
Since 1865

Built by Patrick Tracy for his son Nathaniel, who equipped and sent out the first privateer which sailed from the United Colonies against England. During the revolution he was the principal owner of fifty cruisers which captured one hundred and twenty vessels from the enemy

Here Were Entertained

GEORGE WASHINGTON   MARQUIS de LaFAYETTE
THOMAS JEFFERSON   BENEDICT ARNOLD
JOHN QUINCY ADAMS   AARON BURR

Emma L. Andrews (1852–1928)

Grammar school teacher and Newburyport native Emma L. Andrews cofounded, with school principal Anna L. Coffin, an intimate library in the city's South End in 1900 to serve the children of that community. Originally called the South End Reading Room Association, it was renamed in honor of Andrews following her death.

Newburyporters launched a successful "Emma Forever" campaign in 2010, raising the necessary funds to correct the high lead paint levels that had forced the library's temporary closure in 2009.

Today, the Emma L. Andrews Library and Community Center remains a vial pat of the community, serving both children and adults of the close-knit neighborhood.

Charles Nichols (1942–)

"It started when I looked out my window and noticed there was no flag on the pole," says Charles Nichols. His observation would lead to 16 years of service beautifying the city's Waterfront Park.

Fundraising, landscaping, and caring for flower beds were all interwoven aspects of his job, says the retired Waterfront Park manager. But it is the title of vexillologist, one who studies the symbolism of flags, which Nichols good-humoredly embraces.

George H. Lawler Jr. (1927–2013)

By all accounts, George H. Lawler Jr. was a humble, selfless man who loved and served his community with all his heart. Lawler served as Newburyport's mayor from 1964 to 1967 and served multiple terms as a city councilor prior to, and subsequent to, his mayorship. He also served as city clerk for many years. Lawler's mayoral successor, political rival, and friend Byron J. Matthews once said, "George really gave of himself when it came to helping the city."

It was Lawler who first trounced an urban renewal plan by refusing to sign a federal document authorizing the demolition of the downtown. In an interview with the *Daily News of Newburyport* in 2007, Lawler shared, "It was on my desk. All I had to do was sign it and it was done." Had he signed, Federalist-era buildings would have been lost, replaced with a strip-mall and a parking lot.

Instead, Lawler reached out to the Newburyport Redevelopment Authority and to local preservationists. Through dogged persistence, he brokered a unified force between the two groups that would help safeguard Newburyport's history, ultimately restoring neglected structures and transforming an eyesore of a downtown into a charming and thriving marketplace.

Lawler also helped lead the early efforts of the Newburyport Area Industrial Development in establishing the city's industrial park: The Lord Timothy Dexter Industrial Green. He took great delight in helping organize the city's annual Yankee Homecoming celebration, serving twice as chairperson. From 2002 until his passing, Lawler served as chairperson of the Newburyport Board of Water Commissioners.

Sheriff Frank G. Cousins Jr. says of Lawler's contributions to the community, "Everyone's quality of life here has benefited."

Mary Ann Lawler, who says that her father thought of Cousins as a son, shares that the only thing Lawler loved more than his city was his family. When Lawler died in 2013, Newburyport mourned the loss of its "unsung hero." (Courtesy of Mary Ann Lawler.)

George H. Lawler Sr. (1902–1970) On Friday, April 13, 1951, while guarding the payroll delivery to Towle Silversmiths, Officer George H. Lawler Sr. became a Newburyport hero when he returned the gunfire of five masked robbers, despite being seriously wounded. The brazen holdup remains unsolved. Lawler retired on disability due to a shattered leg that never fully healed. Lawler's son George H. Lawler Jr. is a former Newburyport mayor. (Courtesy of Mary Ann Lawler.)

Mickey (1988–2003)

As feral cat mascot for the Merrimack River Feline Rescue Society (MRFRS), Mickey embodied the heart and soul of the organization's mission to provide care for cats in need.

Mickey was one of the first feral cats that MRFRS volunteers trapped, neutered, vaccinated, ear-tipped (signifying he had been sterilized), and returned to his boatyard home. His shelter was a refurbished doghouse with the words "Mickey's Galley" painted above the entrance.

Over the years, Mickey learned to trust his caregivers, permitting chosen individuals to pet him as he greeted them with a long, throaty "meowww" while they served his meals. The other cats in the colony always deferred to Mickey.

When he grew old, one of his caregivers brought Mickey home to live with her. He adjusted to domesticated life remarkably well, retaining his regal feral "cattitude." (Courtesy of Richard Boisvert.)

Founders of the Merrimack River Feline Rescue Society
From left to right are Sheila Mullins with Thalia the wonder cat, Dorothy Fairweather (first president), Jan DeWitt, Shirley Magnanti, and Nancy MacNeill.

The Merrimack River Feline Rescue Society was founded in 1992 to humanely address Newburyport's feral cat population.

Hundreds of feral cats and kittens had been living along the city's waterfront, many sickly and starving. Through the practice of trap-neuter-vaccinate-return (TNVR), the cats were humanely trapped, sterilized, and vaccinated against rabies. Feral cats were returned to the location of their colonies, fed each day, and provided with shelters. Friendly strays were adopted.

Over the years, attrition took its course with the last remaining feral passing away at age 17.

Today, MRFRS is a nationally known organization, a model for TNVR, and a leader in community outreach, performing discounted sterilizations through its mobile clinic, the Catmobile.

Byron J. Matthews (1928–)

Byron J. Matthews served six years as a city councilor followed by 10 years (1968–1978) as mayor of his beloved hometown of Newburyport. He then served as political advisor to Governor Sargent and as secretary of communities and development under Governor King.

A titan in local government, Matthews took the reins of his predecessor, Mayor George H. Lawler Jr., and continued steering the city toward historic preservation—away from an urban renewal plan that would have bulldozed the downtown.

Because of Matthews's leadership, visitors and locals can stroll along the downtown's red-bricked Inn Street Pedestrian Mall lined with boutiques, cafés, and ice cream parlors, or they can sit and relax on a bench in the bustling Market Square Bullnose.

Matthews's contributions extend beyond the city's center. He is credited with improving the city's tax base by helping to create the Lord Timothy Dexter Industrial Green through his work with Newburyport Area Industrial Development (NAID). Matthews would later serve as president of NAID.

Although the city had approved the industrial park prior to Mayor Matthews taking office, Matthews secured the federal grants to install the park's infrastructure, water, sewerage, and drainage. He spearheaded the construction of the Nock Middle School and expansion of the former Brown School. Matthews was instrumental in the construction of the Water Street seawall, and he secured the necessary funding to build the city's ice rink.

"I was known in this state as the guy who knew how to get the money," Matthews says, referencing the flow of funds he was able to secure for Newburyport during his mayoral tenure.

For his lifelong civic engagement, Matthews was honored as an Essex Heritage Hero in 2010. Also in 2010, Matthews received the Massachusetts Hospital Association's Trustee Excellence in Leadership award for his service to Anna Jaques Hospital.

Matthews's passion for politics and his community is hereditary. "My father loved politics, government, and Harry Truman," Matthews shares. Proud of his Greek heritage, Matthews volunteers each summer at the city's Greek Food Festival.

An obelisk with a bronzed, inlaid image of Mayor Matthews stands in an area dubbed Byron's Court, just off Inn Street. It is not far from where, as a boy, Matthews had a newspaper stand. His greatest satisfaction, Matthews says, comes from the job he did for his city when Newburyport citizens gave him the opportunity to serve as mayor.

Frank G. Cousins, Jr. (1958–)

He credits the interpersonal skills cultivated as a child playing on Perkins Playground, in Newburyport's South End, with serving him as sheriff of Essex County, a position that Frank G. Cousins Jr. has held since 1996. Cousins credits his parents with instilling in him his ideals, sense of civic duty, and the importance of listening to others.

Cousins's father was a former merchant marine with a strong work ethic who always extended a helping hand to neighbors, often placing in his neighbors' hands vegetables from his garden.

When Cousins was a boy, his mother insisted that he accompany her to a speaking event for George Wallace, then governor of Alabama and a candidate for the presidency of the United States.

"I asked her why we should want to listen to this person who doesn't like black people," Cousins recalls. "She said that we were going to hear the governor speak because our responsibility was to listen so that we would know what he was saying and help stop any hate that might come from his words—and to hope that Wallace would change his ways."

Listening is a skill that Cousins actively practices as sheriff. So is the act of doing. He has been an instrumental force in developing behavioral and educational programs to rehabilitate criminal offenders.

Cousins's progressive reforms have made the Essex County Correctional Facility in Middleton, Massachusetts, (the all-male inmate institution that he oversees) a national model. Likewise for the county's first women's prerelease facility, which Cousins helped establish.

But Cousins's contributions are not restricted to the correctional realm. He enjoys reaching into the community to extend a helping hand, like his father before him.

His department's TRIAD program is a partnership between law enforcement and support agencies that seek to prevent seniors from becoming crime victims.

Cousins's Youth Leadership Academy and Junior Leadership Academy are award-winning programs that cultivate personal growth and leadership development through fun activities, bringing young people together in a safe and supportive environment while fostering community spirit. Students receive a graduation certificate upon completion of their program.

"It's important to let young people know that public service is not self-service: they must give to their communities," Cousins says, who is the proud father of a son, Gardner William.

Sharing one of his favorite quotations from author Toni Morrison, Cousins says: "Make a difference about something other than yourselves."

Saira Naseer-Ghiasuddin, MD, FACP (1964–)

At eight years old, Saira Naseer knew that she wanted to become a doctor. As a child growing up in her native Pakistan, Naseer's favorite toy was a make-believe doctor's kit.

"Education was a must in my family," says Naseer, whose late father was an engineer. Her mother, who still lives in Pakistan, kept the household in order and made sure that the couple's children studied undisturbed. Reflecting on her upbringing, Naseer says that the greatest gift her parents gave her was an inheritance of honesty and integrity.

Naseer achieved her goal to become a doctor at age 23, joining an uncle and many cousins on her father's side who were doctors before her. She met her husband, a cardiologist, while the two were medical students in Pakistan. They married and began a family before coming to the United States, eventually settling in Newburyport in 1996.

An internist and primary care physician, Naseer most enjoys her daily interactions with patients. "I like being close to people so that I can help them," she says. Most rewarding for her are the "blessings" she receives from patients, the greatest being patients who have attained and continue to maintain good health under her guidance. When patients require hospitalization, Naseer says, "I won't give up on them. I visit with them and follow them to rehab." For those battling a terminal illness, Naseer says, "I am at my patient's side to the end."

Her wellspring of compassion routinely puts her behind patients' scheduled appointments in her daily practice. "If a patient is sharing something with me, I don't have the heart to interrupt. As a result, I'm not always on time for the next patient," she confesses.

This abundance of empathy, in concert with the thorough medical care she provides, earned Naseer the distinction as the region's No. 1 primary care physician in a 2011 people's choice award. In 2014, she received the Community Clinician of the Year award from her fellow physicians.

Naseer's awards are not restricted to the medical profession, however. Her passion for decorating and historical preservation earned her the Preservation Award for Adaptive Reuse from the Newburyport Preservation Trust in May 2013. The honor acknowledges Naseer's effort in restoring the historic dwelling of her Green Street practice. Its home-like atmosphere is comforting for her patients and gratifying for her, says Naseer.

However, she says that a "thank you" from a patient remains the best award she could ever receive.

Lisa Mead (1962–)

Lisa Mead became Newburyport's first female mayor when she was elected to office in 1993 at age 31, after serving two terms as a city councilor. The Ohio native's victory marked a turning point in what had been a Newburyport-bred male politic. Mead's candidacy received support from the city's gentry, as well as from newcomers to the city like herself. "I think they all saw that I was about making Newburyport a better place for everyone by moving in a professional direction," she states.

Mead praises her mayoral predecessors for their vision and tenacity in implementing a plan of historic preservation in the 1970s, transforming a dilapidated downtown into a city jewel.

But she says that the two decades that followed saw the city decline in its infrastructure and fiscal health. She wanted to do something about it. So she ran for mayor.

Her approach was to operate the city as a professional organization, she explains. Letting her solid financial acumen be her guide, Mead developed a financial plan that restored the city's fiscal stability and allowed for considerable revitalization that included renovations to the high school, police station, library, boardwalk, and Market Square and by bringing new assets to the city such as the MBTA station and the initial funding for today's prized Clipper City Rail Trail.

Of her many accomplishments, one of her proudest is the creation of the Parks Commission. Mead expresses gratitude for the support she received throughout her tenure and praises citizens for getting involved in city issues.

Reflecting on her first mayoral candidacy, Mead recalls the publicity she garnered about being the youngest elected mayor in Massachusetts at the time. "I might have been a little naïve," with regard to the challenges of the corner office, she admits. "I just wanted to do a great job and make sure that city government was accessible to all."

Prior to serving her third term, Mead took a break from Newburyport politics to work for then United States senator John Kerry as his office's state director. "Working for Kerry and bringing state issues to Washington was a fabulous experience," says Mead.

However, Mead's heart song is local government, particularly her backyard of Newburyport.

"No level of government works for its citizens as well as local government," declares Mead. Today, Mead is a partner in a local law firm. (Courtesy of Meg Manion Photography.)

Stephen J. Cutter (1958–)

Firefighting is the lifeblood of Stephen J. Cutter, who retired from the Newburyport Fire Department in 2013 with 34 years of service, the last 12.5 as chief.

His great-grandfather was chief during the 1934 fire that destroyed the downtown's wooden structures; its devastation stretched to the Merrimack River. Cutter's grandfather, who was assistant chief, was the last city firefighter to operate a steam engine. Cutter's father rose to the rank of chief before he retired. "There's been a Cutter in Newburyport firefighting since around 1860," Cutter shares.

He's fought his own share of big fires, including the YMCA and Port Rec fires of the 1980s and the Woodman Way fire of 2006. Pinpointing the most rewarding aspect of his career, Cutter says, "Any time we were able to relieve someone's anxiety and make their day better."

Caleb Cushing (1800–1879)

Cerebral and driven, Caleb Cushing graduated at the top of his Harvard class in 1817 and went on to pursue an illustrious career in law and politics.

After opening a law practice in Newburyport, Cushing served multiple terms as a Massachusetts state representative, a state senator, and a diplomat. As a special envoy to China, he brokered a trade agreement between China and the United States.

In 1851, Cushing was elected Newburyport's first mayor. He also wrote for and edited the Newburyport Herald. Following his mayorship, Cushing served as a justice of the Massachusetts Supreme Court and Attorney General of the United States. During the Civil War, he served as legal advisor in Washington, DC, to Pres. Abraham Lincoln.

Cushing's last years were spent in his Newburyport home. The Caleb Cushing House is a national historic landmark. (Courtesy of the Historical Society of Old Newbury.)

CHAPTER TWO

Community Builders

This chapter offers a glimpse into the lives of some of Newburyport's community builders. Newburyport is a community of activists, driven by fortitude and American spirit. One of the country's most prominent abolitionists, William Lloyd Garrison, was born in Newburyport in 1805. He was passionate in his speech and in his writing as he railed against human slavery. His quest to obtain equal rights for all citizens included his strong support of the women's suffrage movement. A statue of Garrison stands in the city's Brown Square, outside the inn that is named for the famous abolitionist.

Impassioned by his desire to create an open dialog—and love—in his community, the Reverend Bertrand Steeves was not afraid to tackle controversial issues. The retired minister for Newburyport's First Religious Society Unitarian Universalist Church hosted a speaker series that was intended to educate and inspire conversation. In 1961, Steeves invited an expert on extremism to speak to his congregation about the American Nazi party. When they learned the founder of the American Nazi Party planned to crash the event, several hundred citizens lined the sidewalks in solidarity and protest.

Kathleen Bailey is a former Newburyport resident who founded the Field of Honor, a patriotic display of American flags erected each year on the Bartlett Mall. Other Newburyport community builders include Harry O'Connor, beloved Plum Island resident who founded the "World's Shortest St. Patrick's Day Parade"; George A. Cashman, who in 1958 helped found the city's annual multiday summer celebration known as Yankee Homecoming; and Richard Eaton, retired chief executive officer of the Newburyport Five Cents Savings Bank, founding member of the Newburyport Education Foundation, and an indefatigable community volunteer.

Todd C. Woodworth (1921–2006)

A funeral home director for 50 years and owner of the Woodworth Funeral Home, upon his retirement Todd C. Woodworth sold his business to Elliott and Rogers Funeral Home. The merged business became known as the Elliott, Woodworth & Rogers Funeral Home. Woodworth continued to work there part-time.

Woodworth was also a long-distance runner before running became a national pastime; a past chairperson for the city's annual Yankee Homecoming celebration, of which he was crowned king and honored as parade grand marshal as he approached his 80th year; and a tireless historian committed to unearthing and sharing legend and lore of his beloved hometown of Newburyport.

He was the creator of Tiptoe Through the Tombstones with Todd Tours of Oak Hill Cemetery. Woodworth delighted those who accompanied him through the cemetery's forested landscape with tales of sea captains, former mayors, notable writers, abolitionists, and others who have rested there for more than a century. Woodworth's daughter, Ghlee E. Woodworth, a researcher and historian, took up her father's mantle in 2006, continuing the tours and penning a historical book about the cemetery's more legendary inhabitants.

Woodworth shared himself with his beloved community in many ways. Newburyport was in his blood, and it is his blood that he gave to the community. During 57 years as a Red Cross volunteer, Woodworth donated 33 gallons, earning him a record blood donor distinction. He also served as the organization's first local cardiopulmonary resuscitation instructor.

Although Woodworth took his civic duty seriously, the twinkle in his blue eyes was a giveaway to his sense of mirth. He liked to good-naturedly tease people and make them smile.

Woodworth always carried a pocketful of dog biscuits, which he happily doled out to the neighborhood canines. For the humans, Woodworth always had a smile and a friendly, "How ya' doin', kid?" regardless of the person's age. (Both, courtesy of the Newburyport Archival Center at the NPL.)

Grace Jackson Woodworth (1925–2005)
A "behind-the-scenes kind of person," Grace Jackson Woodworth was a former teacher's aide to special needs students for 38 years and a longtime Red Cross volunteer. Her anonymous acts of kindness included providing winter coats to needy schoolchildren and donating bags of food to local pantries, "She was one of many in Newburyport who helped to make this such a caring community," says her daughter, historian Ghlee E. Woodworth. (Courtesy of Ghlee. E. Woodworth.)

George E. Currier, Jr. (1918–2008)
George E. Currier (also known as "Buddy," "Click," and "the Madman") lived on Merrimac Street atop a storefront where he and his wife, Alice, operated many businesses throughout the years.

Currier worked at the Portsmouth Navy Yard from 1941 to 1943 and joined the Seabees as a hardhat diver during World War II. He was appointed a call fireman in 1939 and in 1947 was appointed permanently. In April 1983, he retired after serving 44 years with the Newburyport Fire Department.

In retirement, Currier stayed busy, dabbling in carpentry and home restoration. Once, while painting a three-story home, he tried removing the old paint using a blowtorch. A passerby called 911 on the retired firefighter, reporting a madman who was trying to burn down a house. When officers arrived, they said, "Ah, that's just Click," and drove away.

Currier also worked at the Twomey-LeBlanc Funeral Home for 50 years. He was a fixture at early mass at the Immaculate Conception Church, and he could often be found enjoying fried dough at Market Square or having a Tom Collins at the Park Lunch or Starboard Galley. (Courtesy of Coleen Balent.)

Edward Strong Moseley (1813–1900)
The son of Newburyport lawyer Ebenezer Moseley, Edward Strong Moseley was a shipping magnate, a director of corporations, a philanthropist, a board member for various organizations including the Newburyport Society for the Prevention of Cruelty to Animals, and a president for the Institution for Savings.

During the 1860s, Moseley purchased land along the Merrimack River, creating Moseley Estates. Today, the land is Maudslay State Park. (Courtesy of the Newburyport Archival Center at the NPL.)

Kathleen Bailey (1954–)

"Newburyport has done so much for me," says patriotic community builder Kathleen Bailey. The relationship is reciprocal. Bailey's most moving legacy might be the annual Field of Honor display on the Bartlett Mall. Each year, citizens erect hundreds of American flags for a moving tribute. Bailey founded the event in 2010 to honor those who perished in the 9/11 attacks, for those who serve and protect America, and for those who have lost their lives while serving.

Bailey recalls the first time she stood among the stars and stripes unfurling in the breeze: "I felt like someone had reached down, grabbed my heart, and gently squeezed." In recognition of Bailey's patriotism, the American Red Cross named her a community hero at the organization's annual awards ceremony in 2011.

Although she now lives in Savannah, Georgia, Bailey makes frequent visits back to Newburyport. "In my heart, Newburyport will always be my home," Bailey says. (Above, courtesy of Peter Zoltai.)

Duncan Chase (1919–1980)

With more affection than stigma, Duncan Chase occupies a place in Newburyport's not-too-long-ago past that harbored vagabonds and eccentrics.

A colorful character with a sea captain appearance and sometimes-salty language, he was an oft-inebriated fixture in the city's downtown. Well known for reciting his tag line, "I'm a cool, cool cat!" Chase would invariably let out a loud "meow" afterward.

The portrait of Chase pictured below, which hangs in the Grog Restaurant, was painted by artist Jim Mickelson. (Left, courtesy of the Newburyport Archival Center at the NPL; below, courtesy of the Grog Restaurant.)

Harry O'Connor (1936–1994) Harry O'Connor was the self-installed grand marshal for what he dubbed the "World's Shortest St. Patrick's Day Parade." Deeply proud of his Irish heritage, O'Connor gaily led the two-mile roundtrip procession that began at Plum Island Point and ended with a celebration at his home. The parade's queen, crowned the evening before in an imaginative pageant, rode in the back of Bob Lobster's fish truck. Past queenly luminaries followed in a dump truck. From Miss Seaweed (1978) to Miss Frozen Pipes (1994), 17 ladies earned and then retired their coveted title—including Miss Seagull (1985), who happened to be O'Connor's wife, Charlotte Vincent.

Of her late husband, Vincent says, "Harry lived life with passion and conviction, always with a childlike spirit of adventure and joy." O'Connor was also a newspaperman and founder of the *Plum Island Pages*. (Courtesy of Charlotte Vincent.)

Philip "PJ" Britton (1969–2013)

He was an instantly recognizable Port personality as he rode his motorcycle through town, his blondish locks streaming from beneath a helmet that his mother called "ridiculously small." PJ Britton grabbed life and held it with a Peter Pan embrace, living every moment to a maximum degree.

Britton moved to Newburyport as a child and right away began cultivating his legion of friends. As an adult, he worked construction jobs. An inconspicuous humanitarian, Britton traveled to New York City after the Twin Towers fell on September 11, 2001, to help with the rescue and recovery effort.

Hanging out with his friends whether at the beach, a music festival, or in a local tavern is what Britton most enjoyed. And of course, he loved the freedom he felt riding his motorcycle. (Courtesy of Pam Britton.)

Joseph "Joe" Laite (1959–)

A spirit of giving drives community activist, professional musician, and entrepreneur Joe Laite. He credits his family for his passion for music and for his wellspring of volunteerism. "My mother and father were musicians as well as my brothers and sister," Laite shares. He was four years old when his brother Christopher began teaching Laite to play guitar.

Laite founded the Newburyport Bluescruise and has performed with numerous bands throughout the Northeast. He was a close friend with Regal Queen of the Blues Shirley Lewis. After her passing, he cofounded the Shirley Lewis "Living the Blues" Foundation. A supporter of numerous community causes, Laite successfully initiated the campaign to preserve conservation land adjoining Maudslay Park.

"If I can be instrumental to help someone or something and leave this place better than the way I found it, I'm grateful," says Laite.

Peter "Pete" Falconi (1954–) and Carl Strube (1947–)

As partners of Newburyport-based radio station WNBP-The Legends, Pete Falconi and Carl Strube each bring a passion for the business that began in their youth.

Falconi (left), WNBP's program director, spent his high school years hanging out at his local radio station in Southborough, Massachusetts, observing the on-air personalities. His loitering paid off when Falconi was asked to fill in for a disc jockey who had called in sick. Falconi went on to become a deejay for a Boston top-40 radio station before joining the management ranks for stations in Maine and New Hampshire; he returned to the airwaves with landing a broadcasting job in Boston.

Strube (right), WNBP's general manager, ran a small radio station out of his bedroom in Bath, Maine, when he was only 13 years old. His first paying job was on air in Portland. Strube went on to become an industry consultant for radio stations across the country before becoming an unassuming music mogul. As owner of a record label, Strube represented major acts, including Madonna and Michael Jackson, and was a respected promoter in the music business. Meeting for lunch one day, Falconi and Strube, whose friendship was founded in the industry they shared, decided to share their dream of owning a radio station. In 2009, with the help of local businessman and partner Bob Couture, they purchased WNBP, founded in 1957.

Today, WNBP maintains a local feel with its coverage of human-interest stories, high school football games, news, and sharing "legendary songs from legendary singers."

"We're doing old-school radio," says Falconi. "We're recognized as the local voice of the community." Adds Strube, "Our mantra is commitment to community."

Win Damon (1953–)

Host of WNBP's *The Morning Watch*, Win Damon (a former owner of WNBP) enjoys being the local voice listeners hear as they begin their day. "I like being able to inform people, and I like to make them laugh," says Damon. "But I'm not Milton Berle," he adds, referencing the legendary comedian. Broadcasting the thrill of high school football games is a gem of his job—another is chatting with the citizens whom he interviews.

Debbie Szabo (1950–)

Newburyport High School English and creative writing teacher Debbie Szabo inspires and connects with her students through prose. Creative writing and poetic verse, she tells them, allow humanity to connect with one another on a deep level.

Through her Poetry Soup Club, Szabo's students recite their poems and share their hearts' truths. She started *Poetry Soup Magazine* as a forum for students and alumni to publish work alongside established poets. Szabo also serves as adviser to the *Record*, the school's literary magazine founded more than 100 years ago. She also created Newburyport's Favorite Poem Project. The annual event, held at the Firehouse Center for the Arts, invites local citizens to recite their favorite poem.

In coaching her students for a prestigious poetry slam competition, Szabo instructed them to think about what they were most passionate. "I told them that within three minutes they should be able to sum up what means the most to them," says Szabo.

Szabo's students heeded her advice. Their impressive 2012 finish in the Massachusetts statewide poetry slam, Louder than a Bomb, billed as "the largest teen poetry slam in the world," fills Szabo with pride. Reflecting on the poignancy of her team's performance, Szabo says, "I can still hear them reciting their poems . . . and it still makes me cry." If poetry gives lyric to her soul, social activism drives her spirit. "I try to teach my students that one person *can* make a difference," Szabo states.

For the difference she has made in the Newburyport community and in the lives of her students, Szabo was honored at the city's annual Martin Luther King Jr. Breakfast. She received the 2012 peace award for her efforts to dismantle racism, fight prejudice, and celebrate diversity in the community.

Vicki Hendrickson (1945–)

Tennessee-born Vicki Hendrickson possesses a Southern hospitality accented with Yankee ingenuity. The founder of the Newburyport Literary Festival and director of Newburyport Adult and Community Education, Henderson exudes passion and enthusiasm each time she exhales. Anyone caught in her vortex is quickly drawn into the heart of whatever community project Henderson has embraced. Her ability to inspire and engage others has become legendary.

Anna Jaques (1800–1885)

Anna Jaques was born on her family's Parker River homestead. A frail child, she did not venture far from home; she never married.

Despite her delicate health, Jaques outlived her sister and two brothers. Jaques's brothers had been successful farmers who invested in gold following the Civil War, and Jaques inherited their fortune.

As a witness to the sicknesses that claimed her family, Jaques was inspired to put her wealth to the care and healing of her fellow citizenry. Through her largesse, the Anna Jaques Hospital was founded in May 1884. Jaques died the following January. Originally located inside a federalist mansion on Broad Street, the hospital moved to its Highland Avenue location in 1901 where it continues Jaques's mission to administer care and healing to the Greater Newburyport community. (Courtesy of Anna Jaques Hospital.)

Henry B. Little (1851–1957)
Henry B. Little served as treasurer
to Anna Jaques Hospital and was
a lifelong benefactor. His $1,000
donation to the hospital in 1888
helped establish the School of
Nursing. Little also served more than
half a century as president for the
Institution for Savings, from 1899
through 1953, retiring at age 102.

The industrious and philanthropic
Little attributed his longevity to
family genes and a strong work ethic.
(Courtesy of the Newburyport
Archival Center at the NPL.)

**Marge (1936–) and
Jesse "Skip" (1936–) Motes**
Upon moving to Newburyport in 1995,
Marge and Skip Motes discovered a
hidden treasure: the Newburyport
Art Association. Soon after becoming
members of the organization, the civic-
minded, art-inspired couple began
a quest with Susan Spellman, Alfred
Moskowitz, and others to awaken its
vibrant spirit and extend that spirit into
the community. "We sensed its vast
potential," says Marge.

Marge developed a database that
linked members, donors, and customers,
and she also served as exhibition
chairperson. Her husband Skip fulfilled a
three-year term as the art association's
president followed by terms as treasurer
and secretary.

Membership grew exponentially,
community outreach increased, and the
historic brick building underwent major
renovations, including the addition of the
Laura Coombs Hills Gallery. What had
been "a local art club" was transformed
into a regional art association.

I am aware that many object
o the severity of my language;
t is there not cause for severity?
I will be as harsh as truth, and
as uncompromising as justice.
On this subject,
I do not wish to think,
or to speak,
or write,
with moderation."

WILLIAM LLOYD GARRISON
The Liberator

William Lloyd Garrison (1805–1879)
Newburyport native son and leading abolitionist William Lloyd Garrison held unequivocal and unapologetic views on universal reform, most notably against slavery but also in support of women's suffrage and the rights of Native Americans. His repute earned him the title "the Liberator," which was also apropos to the name of the anti-slavery newspaper he founded and published.

If there was anything that Garrison detested more than social injustice, it was society's inertia in the face of injustice. He once said, "The apathy of the people is enough to make every statue leap from its pedestal and hasten the resurrection of the dead." Indeed, a statue of Garrison looms over Newburyport's Brown Square, in the yard of the inn named after the man. The ardent abolitionist maintains his steadfast stance, poised to make good on his promise. (Both photographs by author, courtesy of Brown Square.)

Richard "Richie" Eaton (1946–)

If home is truly where the heart is, then Richie Eaton—who still lives in the house he grew up in—has never wavered in his love for his hometown of Newburyport. The retired chief executive officer of the Newburyport Five Cents Savings Bank and member of the last graduating class of Immaculate Conception High School is an unassuming community icon, although Eaton would say that he is an ordinary citizen happy to serve his community.

A founding member of the Newburyport Education Foundation, past chairperson of the city's annual Yankee Homecoming celebration, a two-term chairperson of the chamber of commerce, and tireless community volunteer for various causes—including the annual Opportunity Works auction and fundraiser—Eaton's civic wellspring is bottomless. "The community has been very good to me," says Eaton. "It feels good to give back."

A lifelong sports enthusiast, Eaton has shared his passion through 52 years of coaching youth baseball. In 2012, his former employer the Newburyport Five Cents Savings Bank created the Richard A. Eaton Charitable Foundation to assist local young athletes.

Today, Eaton covers high school sports via the local cable station Port Media, and he broadcasts the excitement of Newburyport High School football games over radio station WNBP. The father of three grown sons, uncle to a niece whom he and his wife Kathy raised, and the grandfather to four, Eaton is content to live in his boyhood home with Kathy and their cat Daisy. He still dashes off to board meetings for the many civic organizations that he serves, but Eaton also makes time to play golf and attend Boston Red Sox, Celtics, and Bruins games each year. He's been a season ticketholder to the New England Patriots since 1970.

"I don't live a fancy life," says Eaton. He simply lives the life he loves, in the community that he loves.

George A. Cashman (1925–2006)
In her book *Life in Newburyport: 1950–1985*, author Jean Foley Doyle writes, "George was a man whose life embodied the values that all of us strive for but so few attain."

A past district governor for Rotary International who served on multiple committees, Cashman was a founder of the city's Yankee Homecoming celebration and served as its first chairperson in 1958. He continued on its board of directors for the remainder of his life. Cashman played an influential role in having Newburyport declared the birthplace of the United States Coast Guard. The Coast Guard honored Cashman by presenting him with the Meritorious Public Service Award, the highest honor bestowed upon a civilian.

Recalling her father's "spiritual enthusiasm for life and all of its potential for doing good," Cashman's daughter Christine says, "My father spent his whole life trying to make Newburyport better." (Courtesy of Christine Cashman.)

Betsy (1941–) and Jonathan Woodman (1941–)

In 1972, Jonathan Woodman, a Newburyport native, opened his architectural practice, Woodman Associates, on Inn Street. It was the first of many such restoration projects, as well as new buildings, he and his firm would design. Woodman is also a cofounder of the indoor Racquet Club of Newburyport.

Betsy has published a number of articles and booklets about Newburyport and Salisbury Beach, and the couple has served on numerous boards in the community. For their 50th wedding anniversary, the Woodmans sponsored a jazz concert open to the public, featuring great local musicians. Legendary drummer Les Harris Sr. was honored with a gift to the Newburyport Education Foundation for music in the Newburyport schools. The Woodmans are also generous supporters of the Anna Jaques Hospital.

Rev. Bertrand Steeves (1926–)

During his 38-year tenure as minister for Newburyport's First Religious Society Unitarian Universalist Church (UU), retiring in 1994, Rev. Bertrand Steeves took a bold stand in support of controversial issues of the day.

In 1961, he invited Gordon Hall, an expert on extremism to speak to his UU congregation about the American Nazi party. George Lincoln Rockwell, founder of that party, learned of Hall's engagement and sent a telegram to Steeves saying that he would be attending. Several hundred Newburyport citizens—among them, Holocaust survivors—packed the church and lined the sidewalks on the day of the event. But Rockwell was arrested in a nearby town and never made it to Newburyport. The event provided a great learning opportunity, Steeves says. Subsequent discussion groups were formed to foster open dialog, understanding, respect, and love. The traditions of discussion groups and guest speakers continue with the church today.

When Alabama governor George Wallace, known for his segregationist views, visited Newburyport in 1968 for a presidential campaign stop outside the city's post office, he provoked strong emotions in the crowd who had come to hear him. However, Steeves remembers Wallace's visit for another reason: the Secret Service knocked on his door. "We were having our church steeple painted," Steeves says. "The agents told me that the steeple painter needed to come down so that they could secure access. Apparently, the steeple provided too tempting a vantage point for a potential sniper."

Steeves has his share of folkloric memories, too. He had the esteemed honor of officiating the funeral service for legendary local Duncan Chase, whose tag line was, "I'm a cool, cool cat." Steeves also recalls introducing himself to the city's bad-boy mayor, Bossy Gillis. "I went to visit Bossy at his gas station and said, 'Hello, I'm Reverend Steeves, the new minister at the Unitarian Universalist Church.'" Instead of returning the greeting, Bossy responded: "Yeah, what do you want me to do about it?"

A fair-housing advocate, Steeves worked with Mayor Byron J. Matthews to procure bus transportation for Newburyport's senior citizens. He also helped establish Link House, a residential addiction recovery program for men.

Reflecting on his ministry of "preaching the social gospel," Steeves says, "The greatest reward of being a minister is not accolades or acknowledgements: it's the people."

William Wheelwright (1798–1873)
The personification of "genuine Yankee Grit," William Wheelwright was a merchant, seafaring explorer, US consul, adventure seeker, and Newburyport son. His father was a sea captain.

At the age of 19, Wheelwright commanded a ship sailing for South America. There, he began his exploration for favorable ports of commerce. As a US consul in Ecuador, Wheelwright helped facilitate friendly trade on that country's Pacific coast. His life at sea involved shipwrecks and near drownings. In between his adventurers, he returned to Newburyport, married his sweetheart, and sailed back to South America where the couple settled in Chile. He started a prosperous shipping business that operated steam vessels between South America and Europe.

Wheelwright died in London of an undisclosed illness; his body was shipped back to Newburyport and rests at Oak Hill Cemetery. (Top, courtesy of the Newburyport Archival Center at the NPL.)

CHAPTER THREE

Athletes

Endurance, mettle, altruism, and community spirit are a few of the driving factors of Newburyport's athletes.

Yankee Runner sports-store owner Rick Bayko experienced the pinnacle of his long-distance running career when he completed the historic Athens Classic Marathon in Greece in 2010. Husband and wife team and marathon runners Dale Ann and Dale Bob Eckert run to raise funds for the cure of Alzheimer's Disease. Travis Landreth was on his way to becoming a national running star when his life was cut short due to an undiagnosed heart condition. His sisters, Susannah and Molly, are also accomplished runners who continue to run in memory of their brother.

Many Newburyport runners join the throngs who descend upon the city for the annual Yankee Homecoming 5K and 10-mile road races. Each race begins in front of Newburyport High School (NHS) and ends on the school's 50-yard line of the football field. Each course takes runners past former sea captains' homes on High Street to Water Street where sweeping views of Newburyport Harbor propel them. The 10-mile race passes Maudslay State Park, a favorite spot for local runners with its nearly 500 acres and wooded trails. Maudslay is also the site of Trav's Trail Run, an annual 5K race in honor of Travis Landreth founded by NHS cross-country and track coach Don Hennigar.

Davis Lee is a nuclear physicist and a Triple Crown marathon swimmer. Retired coach James Stehlin has been called the "master architect" of his NHS football team. Retired baseball coach Bill Pettingell, who was recruited by Coach Stehlin, was filled with humility when NHS's baseball field was renamed in his honor.

These individuals, included in this chapter, are only a few of Newburyport's legendary athletes. Others are immortalized on the sports wall of fame at NHS and at the Park Lunch restaurant.

Travis Landreth (1976–2001)

Long distance running sensation Travis Landreth cultivated an impressive resume in his 24 years of life. The former NHS all-scholastic distance runner, United States Junior National Champion in the 5000-meter run, University of Connecticut All-American, and Big East champion in cross-country was pursuing his dream of becoming an Olympian when he collapsed during a training run from an undiagnosed congenital heart condition—he died shortly afterward.

The aspiring Olympian, known for his strong work ethic, warm sense of humor, and acceptance of others, served as inspiration to many—not just to become better runners but to become better human beings.

In Landreth's honor, NHS coach Don Hennigar organized Trav's Trail Run through Maudslay State Park. The annual 5K race draws hundreds of runners, raising money for the Travis Eliot Landreth Memorial Scholarship Fund. (Courtesy of Ruth Landreth.)

Molly Landreth Evak (1982–)
Molly Landreth took inspiration from her big brother Travis to become an elite runner herself. She was the first Massachusetts Division 2 State Cross Country Champion from Newburyport, earned a four-year athletic scholarship to Penn State, and was named Division 1 All American in the steeplechase. Like her sister Susannah, Molly has claimed a title in honor of her brother in the annual Trav's Trail Run. (Courtesy of Don Hennigar.)

Susannah Landreth (1968)
Big sister to legendary distance runner Travis Landreth, Susannah Landreth has made a name for herself as a marathon runner. She is a two-time qualifier for the Olympic Marathon Trials and winner of the Cape Cod Marathon. She is also a constant presence, and fierce competitor, in the many shorter-distance New England road races including Trav's Trail Run, taking a title and honoring her kid brother.

47

Davis Lee (1975–)

For Davis Lee, there is no better way to start the day than with a Plum Island sunrise swim. Snow and darkness are not deterrents. Nor are jellyfish. It was a 21-mile swim off California's Catalina Island in 2011 where he experienced repeated stings from these sea creatures.

Lee, a nuclear physicist, was already one of the English Channel elite, having relied upon his "supreme stubbornness" and stamina to swim the distance between England and France in 2010. Strong currents that pushed him off course, adding 12 miles to the arduous swim for a total of 33 miles, did not stop him. Finishing nearly 13 hours after his start, Lee realized his boyhood dream.

Upon completing the 28.5-mile Manhattan Island marathon swim in 2012, Lee became one of 50 swimming elite to attain Triple Crown status.

William "Bill" Pettingell (1946–)

Bill Pettingell came to Newburyport in 1968 at the invitation of local sports legend and quarterback coach Jim Stehlin to become assistant coach of the freshman football team at NHS. It was the promise of one day coaching baseball that lured him to the Port.

"I always knew that I wanted to coach baseball," Pettingell says. He had enjoyed playing baseball since he was a boy growing up in Natick, playing pickup games in dirt lots, eventually earning All-Scholastic honors at Natick High School under hall of fame baseball coach John Carroll. A baseball scholarship in 1964 to Providence College in Rhode Island followed and served as Pettingell's foundation for his own field of dreams.

He had no idea that nearly a half century later, in 2012, NHS's Lower Field would be renamed the William B. Pettingell Park in honor of the Massachusetts Baseball Coaches Association hall-of-famer who led the Newburyport Clippers to their first Division III state championship in 2011. That same year, Pettingell retired from coaching. He had already led his team to four EMass North and two EMass titles, 18 Cape Ann League titles, and 616 wins in his 40 years of coaching.

Pettingell enjoys telling the story of a 1980 exhibition game that his Clippers played against his alma mater at Doubleday Field in Cooperstown, New York. His former mentor Coach Carroll led the Natick team. A young unknown ball player named Doug Flutie was their relief pitcher. "NHS—that's Newburyport High School—not Natick High School—won 7 to 4!" Pettingell delights in recapping.

Pettingell returned to Natick as an inductee at the 2012 Natick High School Baseball Hall of Fame event. Flutie, now a famous football player, was also there as an inductee. He remembered Coach Pettingell and Natick's humbling loss against the Clippers. "You guys smoked us!" he told Pettingell, paying the coach tribute.

Pettingell also taught history at NHS for 35 years, retiring in 2003. "Teaching is the most noble of professions, by far," he asserts. As he reflects upon his legacy, it's the rapport that Pettingell was able to cultivate with his students in the classroom and on the field that fills him with satisfaction.

Home of the Newburyport Clippers
WILLIAM B. PETTINGELL PARK
Sponsored by THE PROVIDENT BANK   Dedicated 4 August 2012

Beverly (1938–) and James "Jim" (1932–) Stehlin
He has been called "the master architect" of NHS football, having reversed a 20-year losing streak with a Clippers win against Gloucester in 1965. Retired coach Jim Stehlin went on to lead three undefeated teams (1966, 1975, and 1976) and was named coach of the year eight times in his nearly 20-year coaching career. An inductee into the hall of fame for the Massachusetts High School Football Coaches Association, Stehlin inspired a coaching legacy at NHS. He also served as the school's athletic director and social studies teacher until his retirement in 1994. In 2015, the new turf field at NHS's World War Memorial Stadium will be renamed in Stehlin's honor.

"I wanted to create a winning culture of pride and class . . . on the football field and in the classroom," Stehlin says. In 2010, the Newburyport Education Foundation honored Stehlin with its annual Ed Award in recognition of Stehlin's positive influence in the lives of his students. But his number one fan has always been his wife Beverly, who retired after 30 years of service to Anna Jaques Hospital as a hematology supervisor.

Beverly remembers sitting in the stands for the momentous Clippers win against Gloucester. "I got so excited that I slapped the back of the gentleman standing in front of me," she says. "And his false teeth flew out!"

Recalling the response he gave a young waitperson who asked Stehlin, while the couple was celebrating their 50th wedding anniversary with a fine dinner, to share the secret of his long and loving marriage to his wife, Stehlin deadpanned jokingly: "Fear!"

Donald "Don" Hennigar (1952)

Don Hennigar is approaching three decades as NHS cross-country and track coach. He led the boys' cross-country team to its best season in over 50 years with a third-place finish in the 2012 All-States championships and has led the girls' team to three All-States championships.

His numerous athletic awards include Cross Country Coach of the Year from the Massachusetts State Coaches Association. In 2014, Henningar was inducted into the Massachusetts State Track Coaches Association hall of fame. Henningar demonstrates to runners the value of commitment and a good work ethic. "Kids have so much to offer," he states. "They have the potential to do amazing things when they get older."

Coach Hennigar was honored as a Local Legend in 2011. The award, presented by Provident Bank and radio station WNBP, recognizes a community's unsung heroes whose contributions make a profound difference in the lives of others.

Dale Ann (1952–) and
Dale Bob (1956–) Eckert

The Eckerts believe humanity was put on earth to do good. "Everyone can do something to make a difference in the world," says Dale Ann.

Each is a marathon runner; each has had a family member diagnosed with Alzheimer's disease. Together, the couple runs road races—including Newburyport's annual Yankee Homecoming race and the Boston Marathon—representing the national Alzheimer's Association.

"I'm inspired by challenges," says Dale Bob, a cancer survivor who had a heart stent implanted in 2012. Neither condition has stopped him from running for the lives of others.

Dale Ann was just 1.5 miles from crossing the finish line in 2013 when she was forced to turn back because of the Boston Marathon bombing. Returning to the race in 2014, the two were among thousands who reclaimed the finish line for Boston, and for the country, and in honor of those injured and the four who lost their lives in the tragic incident.

Richard "Rick" Bayko (1947–)

Rick Bayko is owner of the Yankee Runner sports store and is a Yankee runner himself. The NHS graduate confides, "I really wanted to be on the baseball team." But Bayko lacked skills "like hitting and catching the ball." So he tried out for the cross-country track team his senior year. Bayko not only found a place on the team, he found his niche as a long-distance runner.

With more than 25 marathons to his sports resume—12 of those the famed Boston Marathon—Bayko experienced the "holy grail" of his running career in 2010. At age 63, Bayko ran the Athens Classic Marathon in Greece. The 2010 race commemorated the 2,500th anniversary of the legendary Greek soldier Pheidippides, who ran nonstop from the town of Marathon to Athens (42 kilometers) in 490 B.C. "It's said to be the first marathon in the world," says Bayko.

Bayko placed seventh in his age division and in the top seven percent overall: 770th out of a field of 12,000. "And I didn't drop dead at the finish line!" Bayko quips, a reference to Pheidippides's fate. (Left, photograph by Tom Gilligan, courtesy of Rick Bayko.)

CHAPTER FOUR

Business Owners

Newburyport is a city of entrepreneurs. Historic entrepreneurs include "Lord" Timothy Dexter and Moses Brown. Dexter was an eccentric legendary local who amassed his wealth through unusual business transactions, such as selling bed-warmers as molasses ladles in the West Indies. Brown was a wealthy merchant who founded a rum distillery on Newburyport's waterfront during the late 1700s. He also established the small city park known as Brown Square and built the stately brick edifice that is today known as the Garrison Inn.

No distilleries remain on Newburyport's waterfront, but the city is home to two new breweries. Chris Webb and Bill Fisher, cofounders of Newburyport Brewing Company, decided to personalize the lid of each can of their beer by etching upon it the Newburyport greeting, "Yeat!"

Bookseller Sue Little is the owner of Jabberwocky Bookshop. Warm and inviting, the store is a haven for book lovers at the Tannery Marketplace.

Dyno Records might seem like it would be a dinosaur; however, owner Richard Osborne has preserved a tie to music history with his selection of vinyl records and has cultivated a loyal customer base.

Bill Bixby is the owner of Ganesh Imports, the bohemian shop that carries wares from his worldwide travels.

The late Nicola "Nick" LaBarba was an Italian immigrant and is the namesake for Nick's Pizza. Since 1957, the pizza shop has been satisfying customer taste buds with Nick's special recipes from the old country.

Curt Gerrish is president and chief executive officer of Rochester Electronics. The successful self-made businessman is also a community philanthropist.

Barbers, pharmacists, coffee shop owners, tavern owners, corner store owners, and a "raconteur sea captain" are some of the other individuals from Newburyport's business community who are captured in this chapter.

William "Bill" Bixby (1961–)

Bill Bixby describes himself as "one or two parts hippie." The cool proprietor and purveyor of Ganesh Imports is also a savvy entrepreneur, humanitarian, de facto cultural ambassador, and world traveler.

Bixby grew up in Haverhill, Massachusetts, where his grandfather and father worked in the family business, Bixby International. The plastics manufacturer, now located in Newburyport, began as a supplier to the footwear industry in the late 1800s. Although Bixby did not go into the family business, it was his grandfather who instilled in him wanderlust for far-flung locales. Bixby was an impressionable fourth-grader when his grandfather took him on a trip to Africa. After graduating from college, Bixby traveled around the world for a year, immersing himself in a simple, vagabond life while embracing each rich experience. He once hiked two weeks into the bush of Papau New Guinea, arriving at the tribal land of two warring tribes—site of the rumored cannibalized demise in 1961 of Michael Rockefeller, youngest son of former vice president Nelson Rockefeller.

Bixby started collecting artifacts from the various countries that he visited, conducting transactions with natives, whom he calls his "Ganesh family," and establishing cultural relationships that endure today.

His hip boutique, named after a Hindu deity, is stocked with wares from his travels to Thailand, Indonesia, Central America, India, Nepal, and Mexico. It was his cultural love affair with these lands and a desire to introduce others to these cultures that inspired Bixby to open Ganesh Imports in 1989.

When a devastating tsunami hit Thailand in 2004, Bixby felt compelled to help. "I didn't personally know anyone who was injured, but I wanted to do something for the communities that were impacted," Bixby says. So he held a one-day "sale-athon" and donated 100 percent of the day's proceeds to Thailand's tsunami relief effort.

Following his grandfather's legacy, Bixby is planting the seeds of cultural wanderlust in his teenage son Liam who accompanied Bixby on a buying trip to Guatemala. While there, Bixby introduced Liam to his Ganesh family.

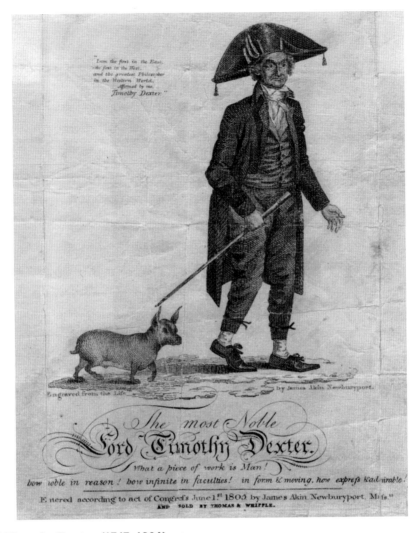

From the first in the East, the first in the West, and the greatest Philosopher in the Western World. Affirmed by me. Timothy Dexter.

Engraved from the Life. *by James Akin Newburyport.*

The most Noble Lord Timothy Dexter.

What a piece of work is Man! how noble in reason! how infinite in faculties! in form & moving, how express & admirable!

Entered according to act of Congress June 1st 1805 by James Akin Newburyport. Mass."
AND SOLD BY THOMAS & WHIPPLE.

"Lord" Timothy Dexter (1747–1806)

He might be Newburyport's most eccentric legendary local. Lord Timothy Dexter—he bestowed the noble title upon himself—moved to Newburyport from Malden, Massachusetts, as a young man to pursue a vocation as a tanner. Shortly after his arrival, Dexter married a wealthy widow whom years later he would berate for not wailing adequately at his self-staged mock funeral. With his wife's seed money, Dexter engaged in various business dealings to amass a fortune. Whether his success was due to acumen or fool's luck is debatable. Selling bed warmers as molasses ladles in the West Indies and importing feral cats to the Caribbean Islands as rodent controllers were two of Dexter's bizarre and wildly successful ventures.

His investment in devalued American Revolutionary War currency added to Dexter's fortune when, at the war's end, he collected its worth from the government. Dexter shared his success story with his fellow citizens in *A Pickle for the Knowing Ones*, a book he wrote and published, absent of punctuation and fraught with misspellings.

With a small, hairless dog as his walking companion, Dexter cut a curious, if not lordly, figure as he strode through Newburyport wielding a cane, wearing a three-cornered velvet hat, a brightly colored topcoat, scarlet trousers, and Persian shoes with turned-up toes. (Courtesy of the Newburyport Archival Center at the NPL.)

Bruce Vogel (1952–)

A marathon runner, a Newburyport city councilor, and a flight attendant during the disco era, Bruce Vogel has settled into his role as Newburyport's boatyard coffee czar as owner of Plum Island Coffee Roasters. The aromatic coffee that he serves is from roasted Arabica beans; the sometimes-salty banter he offers is an extension, or shtick, of his alter ego as a stand-up comic.

Guided by his philosophy "to give back and to leave something," Vogel's contributions to the community include helping to establish the Department of Youth Services, helping to preserve 100 acres of the city's Common Pasture, and serving Newburyporters really good coffee.

John Magro (1951–)

John Magro is the low-key, affable, former owner of Newburyport's corner store, Richdale, at the intersection of State and Pleasant Streets. In addition to carrying typical general store items, Richdale is famous for its 25¢ hot dogs and penny candy selection. Tourists love the Newburyport-emblem clothing.

"Getting to know everyone has been the best part of the business," says Magro, who retired and sold the store in 2014. Richdale's neighborhood atmosphere has fostered friendships between Magro and many of his local customers.

Nicola "Nick" LaBarba (1926–1997)

In 1957, Nick LaBarba and his wife, Gilda, natives of Canosa Sannita (Abruzzo), Italy, took over a small family restaurant housed inside a nondescript Merrimac Street dwelling, renamed it Nick's Pizza, and began making rectangular pizzas from their Italian recipes. Nick's presence can still be felt; photographs of the founder adorn one wall. The original wooden booths and a 1950s jukebox remain.

"My father was a quiet, good, hard-working man, who worked seven days a week at two jobs all of his life until he retired," says his son Frank. "All of the locals in town, both young and old, liked my father." Nick's legacy continues. The multigenerational business, run by Frank and his wife, Tiziana, is patronized by generations of neighborhood customers and those from miles away. (All, courtesy of Frank LaBarba.)

William G. Taplin (1937–)

William G. Taplin, also known as Captain Bill, guided passengers aboard his *Yankee Clipper* through Newburyport harbor for 26 years. Donning a braided wig or a lobster-claw hat, he regaled them with songs, legends, and salty tales.

The friendly, seafaring, song-singing raconteur's familiar and booming refrain, "Harbor Tours, now boarding!" was an invitation to all who strolled Newburyport's boardwalk.

He recalls a story from his whale's tail of amusing anecdotes. While returning to the harbor one day, Taplin issued a spurious captain's order. "I said what I always say as I prepare to dock: 'Anyone over four-feet tall should jump ship and swim the rest of the way.'" Passengers responded with the usual laughter—except for two gentlemen (who, Captain Bill speculates, may have been enjoying private cocktails). They jumped overboard. "Fortunately, the Coast Guard was directly behind me with an inflatable raft," recalls Taplin, "and the officers were able to quickly pluck the gentlemen from the harbor."

Taplin's irrepressible humor and joy for life influence his entire world. The former schoolteacher once brought a watermelon to the classroom and engaged his young students in a seed-spitting contest. The student who spit the most seeds into the center of the room was declared the winner. "I'd probably be fined for doing that today," Taplin says.

His teaching life was stoked while he was a counselor at Camp Sea Haven, a retreat for polio-afflicted children, on Plum Island during the 1950s. The school's director observed Taplin's talent for working with children and told him that he'd make a good teacher, "something I had no intention of becoming," Taplin says. He retired from teaching with 34 years of service.

After selling his *Yankee Clipper* to a fellow boater in 2006, Taplin took the helm at Plum Island Ecotours. He kept the business until 2011, gliding his vessel, the *Joppa Flats*, through the estuaries of the Great Marsh, bringing the wonder of the Parker River National Wildlife Refuge to his passengers. Taplin is presently working to make his next venture a reality: creating a ferry that would transport passengers between Salisbury Beach State Reservation and Newburyport.

The father of 8 and grandfather to 14, Taplin reveals that his greatest accomplishment has been marrying his wife, Ellen. Love, he says, is his life's philosophy.

John Farley Allison (1943–)

John Farley Allison is Newburyport's debonair haberdasher. As the proprietor of John Farley Clothiers, Allison has cultivated sophistication in his gentlemen clientele since 1988. He was honored as Retailer of the Year in 2008 by the Greater Newburyport Chamber of Commerce and Industry.

A past president of the city's chamber of commerce and a foundation board member of Anna Jaques Hospital, Allison's contributions to the community go beyond offering custom-made suits. Allison offers himself. He once shaved his head as part of a fundraiser for the rehabilitation of a young man who had suffered a spinal cord injury.

An outdoor enthusiast, Allison has climbed Mount Rainier—twice. At age 60, he took up downhill skiing.

In 2014, Allison announced he would be retiring and closing up shop. In an interview with *Newburyport Today* in 2012, he reflected on what he has most enjoyed: "Having the store is like having company in the house . . . many of my customers have become my good friends."

Cynthia Meade (1936–) and Gina Wilson (1967–)

Mother and daughter team Cynthia Meade and Gina Wilson serve cappuccino, espresso, tea, and pastry with a helping of townie panache. The co-owners of Caffe di Siena enjoy fostering a culture of community where locals and visitors to Newburyport are warmly welcomed. "We love that our café is a place where customers can relax and interact in an old-world way," says Wilson.

Esther Sayer (1949–)

"My main contribution is making Newburyport more beautiful by sprucing up our men," teases Esther Sayer. The owner of Inn Street Barber and Styling Shop has been wielding cutting shears over the heads of her mostly male clientele since 1981.

"I want this to be a fun place to get a haircut," states the merry brunette who grew up in Lawrence, Massachusetts.

Each December, Sayer throws a bash for her "barber shop family." Dubbed the Hair Ball, the event is Sayer's way of saying thank you to her employees and loyal customers. Sayer's humor, warmth, and generous spirit have endeared her to locals. Whether raising funds for charitable organizations as a celebrity bartender or as a thespian (she read a part in *The Vagina Monologues*), Sayer has mastered the art of having fun while helping her adopted community.

Francis Todd (1779–1861)

Newburyport ship owner Francis Todd found himself a subject in the "Black List," an 1829 newspaper column penned by abolitionist and fellow Newburyporter William Lloyd Garrison, printed in *The Genius of Universal Emancipation*. Garrison accused Todd of using one of his ships to transport slaves, a charge that Todd denied. Garrison called for Todd's lifetime confinement, but it was Garrison who was jailed for libel— despite evidence indicating that Todd engaged in at least one slave voyage.

Capt. Francis B. Todd (1805–1841)

Interred in a barrel of rum at Oak Hill Cemetery lies Capt. Francis B. Todd. The son of Francis Todd met his demise in Cuba after contracting yellow fever. Captain Todd had sailed on his father's ship, the *Francis*, which William Lloyd Garrison had accused the elder Todd of using to traffic in human slavery.

Peter G. Kelly

Peter G. Kelly is the humble and unpretentious proprietor of Kelly's True Value Hardware, a business that his father cofounded as Lunt & Kelly Hardware in 1946.

"My father treated everyone with respect . . . he remains my greatest inspiration," Kelly says. When Mr. Lunt, his father's business partner retired, Kelly came onboard. He promised his father two years. "But the business grew on me," Kelly says, "and I liked the idea of being here for my community."

Community is the foundation of this family institution, where customers can purchase a wrench while reconnecting with a neighbor or friend whom they have not seen for awhile. Interacting with his customers is the highlight of Kelly's day. He loves the mix of families, townies like himself, and newer citizens to the community. Kelly is delighted that his hardware store serves them all.

Steven Fram (1947–)

Steven Fram filled prescriptions and doled out townie quips as a pharmacist at Eaton's Drug Store, which stood on the corner of State and Pleasant Streets from the early 1900s until 1988. Fram's father, himself a pharmacist, had purchased the neighborhood institution in 1962 and kept the name of its first owner. In addition to his pharmacist role, Steven Fram served 18 years as Newburyport director of public health.

Nancy Langsam (1947–) and Andrew Mungo (1949–)

When Newburyport's unassuming priest and priestess of cinema, Andrew Mungo and Nancy Langsam, opened the Screening Room in 1982, they created an intimate and alternate film universe with their 99-seat movie theater, distinct from cinema complex behemoths.

The two met at a Newburyport social event in the late 1970s. Upon discovering that they each held a mutual desire to "establish themselves in a project of their own design," one that would also sustain them, they pursued their celluloid dream. "I've always loved movies," says Langsam, "and I wanted to share this interest."

Langsam selects the independent films that are screened in the living-room-like theater. A native of Long Island, New York, Langsam graduated from New York University where she majored in government and minored in English; she moved to the Port in 1975.

"It was a whim gone awry," Mungo deadpans of the pair's cinematic venture. He greets filmgoers while handing them admission tickets. A native of Lawrence, Massachusetts, after he graduated from Lawrence High School, Mungo pursued a seven-year, vagabond, self-guided trek of Western Europe and Polynesia, pit stopping in New York City where he drove a Checker Cab, before crashing in 1976 at the cheapest place he could find on the North Shore: Plum Island. In his mind's eye, Mungo rewinds the Screening Room's film reel to share the story behind the theater.

He recalls being "tossed" from the chamber of commerce, where he and Langsam had sought early support for their venture. "He thought we were a couple of dirty, old hippies," Mungo states of the gentleman who showed them the door. "Speak for yourself!" Langsam interjects. "Oh, sorry . . . a couple of dirty, young hippies," Mungo corrects himself.

Five years of fits, false starts, and tribulations would follow. "We were the laughing stock," Mungo says of the reputation he and Langsam had unwittingly cultivated through their many attempts to open a theater. But the persistent duo did not give up; they raised the necessary funds to finally see their dream realized. When outdated equipment threatened the Screening Room's future in 2013, the community rallied around Langsam and Mungo. Through a successful fundraising campaign, the film duo was able to purchase a digital film projector. With its living-room-like ambiance and supportive local moviegoers, the Screening Room remains an enduring icon in the Port's pop culture.

Curtis L. "Curt" Gerrish (1936–)

Curt Gerrish is president and chief executive officer of Rochester Electronics, the last serving president of the dissolved Newburyport Area Industrial Development organization, and a philanthropist. Gerrish developed his work ethic as a youth growing up in Newburyport. "I saw hard-working people, individuals who took care of themselves and their families, people who recognized the value in doing," he says. As a young man, Gerrish helped in his parents' restaurant, the Flying Yankee (which morphed into Joseph's Winter Street Café and is now Andiamo).

Gerrish is intent on helping young people access their potential. Rochester Electronics's summer intern program for at-risk youth instills positive values, a solid work ethic, and teaches the connection between working and earning a living.

The Gerrish Family Foundation provides assistance to community-serving institutions that include Anna Jaques Hospital, the Immaculate Conception School, and Endicott College in Beverly. In 2013, Endicott dedicated its new school of business as the Curtis L. Gerrish School of Business.

Donald McKay (1810–1880)

Legendary shipbuilder Donald McKay was born in Nova Scotia and traveled to New York in 1826 where he worked for a master shipbuilder as an indentured laborer. He arrived in Newburyport in 1839 with his head full of imaginative and innovative designs for the clipper ships—fast merchant vessels—that he sought to create.

Finding work with Newburyport shipbuilder John Currier before eventually opening his own shipyard in Boston, McKay's genius shone in the golden era of maritime power. His ships were regarded for their beauty, durability, speed, and creative names. The *Flying Cloud*, at nearly two tons, and the *Sovereign of the Seas*, more than two tons, encountered battering storms that made the voyages harrowing for their respective crews. However, each ship arrived at its destination intact.

McKay and his clipper ships remained a force until the advent of steamships following the Industrial Revolution in this country.

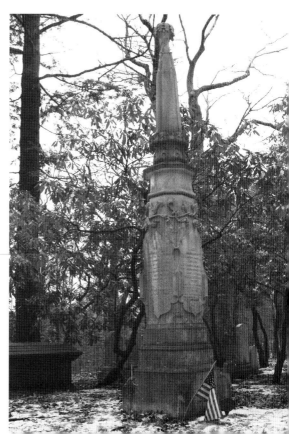

Cyrus Rogers (1978–)

"There are no zombies," Cyrus Rogers emphatically and light-heartedly states, putting to rest the legends and lore of the undead. Living above his family-owned Elliott, Woodworth & Rogers Funeral Home, which dates back four generations, Rogers, a mortician, says "bumps in the night" are simply old-house noises. The tales he shares are about humanity.

"Taking care of those I know, or someone who is young and who should have had a long life ahead, can be rough," Rogers says of the deceased who are entrusted to him. "I try to help families through tough times as they cope with the loss of their loved ones." To sooth his own soul, Rogers listens to classical music. "It helps rid my mind of clutter," he says. Rogers is also a musician; he plays bass guitar in several local bands.

ELLIOTT
WOODWORTH
PAUL C. ROGERS FAMILY
FUNERAL HOME

65

Charlene Ferreira (1959–) and Glenn Mayers (1955–)
As co-owners of Glenn's Restaurant and Cool Bar, husband-and-wife team Charlene Ferreira and Glenn Mayers are a combination of warmth and class, sass and spice—like the signature dishes they serve.

Mayers's hat-wearing proclivity is stylin'. Before he begins simmering his sauces, Mayers dons a hat that is silly, colorful, hip, gangsta, or something else that complements his mood.

"He's just like Lady Gaga," Ferreira delights in saying, comparing her husband to the costume-changing singer and provocateur. For fans of R&B, jazz, and soul—in addition to haute cuisine—the couple hosts a Sunday Soul series in their very cool bar. The spiritualizing event features amazing local talent led by blues harmonica player Justin Quinn. Glenn's also hosts an annual fundraiser for a local equine rescue group.

Bill Fisher (1975–) and Chris Webb (1970–)

Promising a great beer in a can and great adventure, Bill Fisher (left) and Chris Webb (right), fun-loving cofounders of Newburyport Brewing Company, are on a mission to make people happy. "We've melded our love of beer and music with our love of Newburyport," says Webb.

Green Head IPA, "the beer that bites you back," is a tribute to the greenhead horsefly that leaves welts on Plum Island beachgoers each summer. Newburyport Pale Ale and Plum Island Belgian White complete the brewers' three signature brews. The Newburyport greeting, "Yeat!" is etched on the lid of each can of beer. Included with each six-pack is a guitar pick, because "you always need one" says Fisher.

Both Fisher and Webb play in the Newburyport funk band Das Pintos— performing often for community fundraisers and, occasionally, on stage at their own brewery.

Michael "Mike" Doyle (1947–)
Mike Doyle is proprietor and cultural custodian of Newburyport's fabled Park Lunch, the family restaurant and neighborhood sports tavern that townies and out-of-towners have flocked to since Doyle purchased the business in 1969. Doyle is proud to have preserved the Park Lunch's inimitable character, even after a fire in 2004 necessitated the building's renovation. Its sports wall of fame features pennants and photographs of local legends; a photograph of Doyle from 1962 hangs on the wall.

Calling his wife, Jean, "the brains of the operation," Doyle doles out compliments when speaking about his loyal staff that includes generations of family. Gregarious and loquacious, Doyle loves to chat with and occasionally tease his customers. He is fond of wearing his "No Bloviating" T-shirt in jest.

"At the Park Lunch, you can come in and feel like you are at home in your neighborhood," says Doyle.

Gabrielle Minh (1951–)

Gabrielle Minh grew up in a prominent family in South Vietnam. She led a comfortable life—until the fall of Saigon. Her husband Dan was an officer with the South Vietnamese military. He was one of hundreds of thousands of men rounded up by the North Vietnamese Army and sent to communist re-education camps.

When finally permitted a visit with her husband, three years into his imprisonment, Gabrielle recalls, "I did not recognize him. I thought, 'My God who is this dead body?'" Gabrielle learned the value of a bribe. In exchange for gold "donations" to prison guards, she was allowed to bring food to her husband. When Dan was finally released 7.5 years later, he and Gabrielle began plotting their family's escape from Vietnam. They wanted to raise their children in America where they would have freedom.

Through a cousin who had left Vietnam years earlier and was living in Texas, Gabrielle reached out to an American pastor. Fr. John F. Leonard had been stationed in Gabrielle's village, where he taught English to local children. Gabrielle had been one of his brightest pupils. Gabrielle's cousin located the priest at Newburyport's Immaculate Conception Parish, where he was pastor. Father Leonard welcomed the opportunity to sponsor Gabrielle and her family.

Dan escaped Vietnam by boat in 1985 with the couple's middle son; Gabrielle remained behind so she could bribe authorities for Dan's safe passage. Three years would pass before Gabrielle and the couple's other two sons could join Dan. Their escape was harrowing. Crammed into a small boat with more than 100 other refugees, they were one week at sea without food or water before docking at a small island. As they boarded another boat, communist guards fired upon them. Gabrielle and her children lived in refugee camps in Indonesia and the Philippines before eventually arriving in Newburyport in 1988. Just three months after her arrival, Gabrielle opened Minh's Tailor Shop, located today in Newburyport's Tannery Marketplace. She and Dan bought their home in 1995 in neighboring Salisbury.

"Life's purpose is to love people," Gabrielle says. She explains that her ordeal taught her to love—rather than hate. "I respect the life spirit in all creatures," says Gabrielle, who embraces a vegan philosophy and is Buddhist.

Sue Little (1950–)

Bookseller Sue Little created an intimate literary nook when she opened a tiny bookstore in downtown Newburyport in 1972. She was just 22 years old. Jabberwocky Bookshop moved to a larger space in the Tannery Marketplace in 1986. Little's original customers followed, and new customers arrived. Today, the store remains a haven for book lovers.

Floor-to-ceiling shelves (which Little helped build) line the walls. Bookcases sit at juxtaposed angles across the floor, creating parallel literary portals that invite Jabberwocky's clientele to browse. Browsing, Little believes, is an art form—one that she joyfully encourages.

Books of poetry, cooking, gardening, and a myriad of other subjects—including an extensive selection of fiction, a testament to Newburyport's many authors—beckons customers. Thousands of bargain books—publishers' overstock that Jabberwocky offers at discount prices—can be found throughout the store. "We scour publishers' lists for books that are the best and most amazing," says Little. The adjacent Green Room offers an impressive selection of "once-read" books. A children's loft holds tomes for younger readers.

Little's mother has also been in on the family fun. She has worked the cash register at Jabberwocky for more than 25 years. Little's two children, now grown, spent a good chunk of their childhood in the store. Even Little's cat took up residence.

Offering a respite from the harried world, with promises of enchantment through the written word, Jabberwocky's success continues in an age of electronic publishing.

"Though we started small, today we are one of only a handful of larger bookstores left in New England," Little shares. The store's Friday-night author series brings local and regional authors together with local book lovers. Each year, Jabberwocky becomes a major venue for the Newburyport Literary Festival, hosting between 30 and 40 authors in one day.

"Bringing people and books together is what Jabberwocky is about," says Little.

When she's not at Jabberwocky, Little can be found at her bucolic, ancestral farmstead in neighboring Newbury. She is the 10th generation of her family to live on the farm, founded around 1640.

Richard Osborne (1952–)

Dyno Records has been a Middle Street landmark since 1976, when owner Richard Osborne filled his store with vinyl albums and opened the door. "One of my great joys in life is hearing something that is unlike anything I've heard before," says Osborne, who derives great pleasure in sharing his passion. Today, an assortment of CDs from various artists complements the inventory. Osborne's store has become a destination for customers in love with the sound, packaging, and allure of vinyl records.

Michael Roy (1941–)

He served as a US Army counter-intelligence special agent stationed in Europe during the 1960s. "My mission was to catch a spy and turn him into a double-agent," says Michael Roy. But the man who is now a caregiver to four docile alpacas and two dogs on a quiet Newbury lane is best known for the Newburyport landmark that bears his name: Michael's Harborside.

Roy purchased the run-down waterfront property in the 1970s, transforming it into a popular restaurant and bar. He sold the business and the building in 1999 but not before establishing a Yankee Homecoming tradition. "Michael's Harborside paid for the first Yankee Homecoming fireworks show," he proudly shares.

Although he hosted famous personalities including Goldie Hawn, Kurt Russell, and Ted Kennedy in his restaurant, Roy says his interactions with everyday customers and staff members are memories that he treasures most. (Below, courtesy of Edith Heyck.)

Harold Boothroyd (1945–)

Barber Harold Boothroyd has been cutting hair at the Razor's Edge since 1966—he purchased the business in 1977. His neighborhood shop is reminiscent of the barbershop from Mayberry, the fictional town of the 1960s television show *Mayberry R.F.D.* "Just don't call me Floyd," Boothroyd admonishes, referencing the television barber.

His eldest customer, a gentleman in his 80s, was also his first. Boothroyd's customers span family generations. One family includes five generations; the youngest was five weeks old when Boyd gave him his first haircut. One day each week, Boothroyd leaves his shop to cut the hair of seniors residing in nursing homes or those who are home but infirmed.

Following the Yankee Homecoming road race each year, his shop's small parking lot is the scene of a neighborhood celebration. "I'm an official water stop for the road race," Boothroyd shares. "I love being here."

Richard Simkins (1941–)
Richard Simkins is one of Newburyport's most everlasting restaurateurs as proprietor of one of Newburyport's most legendary landmarks: the Grog.

Since purchasing the business in 1970, Simkins has transformed what began as a post–Civil War saloon for sailors and statesmen to a destination restaurant for locals and tourists. Today's Grog clientele enjoys an extensive selection of craft beer, signature dishes, and live musical entertainment.

Taking its name from the British navy's drink of rum and water, the Grog is steeped in history—and mystique. Simkins enjoys telling the tale of Adm. Edward Vernon, nicknamed "Old Grog." Vernon commandeered a fleet of British sailors during the War of Jenkins's Ear in 1739 to capture a Spanish port. His portrait hangs in the Grog's main dining room. As the "Grogfather," Simkins is a figure in Newburyport's lore.

John Newmarch Cushing (1820–1904)

John Newmarch Cushing was the son of a sea captain. Joining his father's trade merchant business, Cushing became co-owner of a fleet of ships and of one of Newburyport's largest shipyards, Cushing's Wharf.

Cushing's half-brother Caleb served as Newburyport's first mayor. A Federalist-style mansion on stately High Street, once home to three Cushing generations, is today home to the Historical Society of Old Newbury, a National Historic Landmark. (Courtesy of the Historical Society of Old Newbury.)

Moses Brown (1742–1827)

Entrepreneur Moses Brown founded his own carriage manufacturing business when he was 20 years old. He later invested in shipbuilding and in the lucrative sugar and molasses trade of the West Indies, making him a very wealthy man. Brown established a rum distillery on Newburyport's waterfront and built a stately brick building that survived Newburyport's great fire of 1811. This building today is the Garrison Inn, located in Brown Square.

Brown is credited with helping to get the US Navy afloat after losses from the Revolutionary War left it dead in the water. With other wealthy Newburyporters, Brown financed the building of warships, which they turned over to the government for reimbursement in a subscription ship program.

A philanthropist, Brown's large donations helped establish the Brown Latin High School. He also funded the theological seminary in Andover, Massachusetts. (Photograph by author, courtesy of Brown Square.)

Louis (1936–) and Stella (1941–) Andriotakis

As co-owners of D.L. Lynch Pharmacy, the neighborhood apothecary and Port institution, husband-and-wife team Stella and Louis Andriotakis greet their customers, who include generations of families, by name.

The pharmacy is a pleasant throwback to a bygone era. Louis fills prescriptions while standing on a raised platform behind a spindle-slatted wooden window through which Stella, who manages the operation, slides completed orders to customers.

Lynch's is one of the few pharmacies in the area that offers compounded fish- and chicken-flavored medications, appealing to canine and feline clientele. The pharmacy also carries an extensive selection of homeopathic remedies and all-natural products. Stella and Louis have been providing their customers with personalized health care since 1967 (when Louis purchased the business), bringing care and warmth to each customer transaction.

Nathaniel Tracy (1751–1796)

Harvard-educated Nathaniel Tracy was a prosperous merchant and ship owner who hosted the country's political royalty in his home, the Tracy Mansion, now home of the Newburyport Public Library. Thomas Jefferson and George Washington were among the luminaries lavishly entertained. Tracy was also a devoted patriot. During the Revolutionary War, Tracy parlayed his resources to become a major financier of the American Revolution and a successful privateer. Outfitting a number of his vessels as warships, Tracy's fleet captured more than 100 enemy vessels. Eventually, however, the British grew weary of Tracy's ransacking, which had become a threat to their supply line. So they blockaded Newburyport's harbor, sounding the death knell on Tracy's fleet and his fortune.

By the end of the war, most of Tracy's ships had been lost at sea, shipwrecked, or captured. (Courtesy of the Newburyport Archival Center at the NPL.)

CHAPTER FIVE

Literary and Visual Artists

Writers and artists are Newburyport's ubiquitous citizens. The Newburyport Literary Festival, founded in 2006, celebrates the city's rich literary heritage. In 1860, Newburyport author Harriet Prescott Spofford wrote a Gothic short story that impressed and unsettled famous poet Emily Dickinson. J.P. Marquand, who grew up at Curzon's Mill just beyond Maudslay State Park, won a Pulitzer Prize for his social satire *The Late George Apley*. Marquand was honored at the 2010 Newburyport Literary Festival.

Other festival honorees have included the Dominican-born, award-winning poet Rhina Espaillat and the award-winning, Irish-born writer Áine Greaney.

Former Newburyporter Tom Ryan is author of the best-selling *Following Atticus*, Ryan's poignant memoir of self-discovery while hiking New Hampshire's White Mountains with his canine companion Atticus M. Finch.

Newburyport's artist lineage includes Laura Coombs Hills, a successful miniature portrait painter, and portrait and landscape artist Sam Sargent, who founded the Newburyport Art Association in 1948.

Expressionist artist Edith Heyck moved to Newburyport in the 1970s, finding inspiration in cityscapes and nearby marshes. Artist Alan Bull paints nudes, murals, monotypes, landscapes, and nautical scenes. However, he might best be known for his paintings of old trucks, which he asserts are part of Americana. The city's local art galleries share and celebrate art with the community through regular art walks that invite people to stop in. Newburyport's literary and visual arts community includes more than writers, poets, and painters. A bead artist, a paper-cutting artist, a model shipbuilder, an Emmy Award-winning journalist whose current passion is photography, playwrights, journalists, historians, and others have captured, and been captured by, Newburyport and have called the city home.

John P. Marquand (1893–1960)

In her biography of author John P. Marquand, Millicent Bell writes, "His was a profoundly American life." It was Marquand's life in Newburyport—the prism through which he peered in writing his book about Newburyport's "Lord" Timothy Dexter, later turning that prism inward to write his Pulitzer Prize-winning *The Late George Apley*—that profoundly imprinted the social satirist.

Marquand spent his boyhood in the home of his eccentric aunts in Curzon's Mill, just beyond Maudslay State Park, and graduated from Newburyport High School. His ancestors were prosperous Federal-era merchants who lost their properties in Newburyport's 1811 fire. Marquand's father lost his business in the stock market crash of 1907.

The social arrogance of America's upper social class was a theme of Marquand's novels. He also wrote for the *Saturday Evening Post* and created the *Mr. Moto* spy novels. (Courtesy of Beth Welch.)

Alfred Nicol (1956–)

Alfred Nicol describes his work as a poet as an "intense physical encounter with the written word." If he has done his job well, Nicol says, his readers will also experience this physicality.

He explains that a poem's whole meaning—its truth—is shaped by its cadence and the music that underlies it. "I'm always listening for the language beneath the language," he states. "It's the musical sound of words—more than what is said by the words."

Nicol is a recipient of the prestigious Robert Frost Poetry Award (first prize, 2013) for his poem, *Mid-November House Guest*; the title poem from his 2006 collection *Elegy for Everyone* earned him first prize from the New England Poetry Club, and he received the Richard Wilbur Award in 2004.

Nicol's poems have been published in acclaimed literary journals and anthologies. He is a member of the Newburyport-based Powow River Poets, and he also performs in the poetic musical ensemble Melopoeia with poet Rhina Espaillai, classical guitarist John Tavano, and soprano Ann Tucker.

Joel Brown (1959–)

A journalist for the *Boston Globe* covering arts and culture, Joel Brown (a Newburyporter since 1998) is also a novelist. He has created a cult following with *Mirror Ball Man*, *Mermaid Blues*, and *Revolution Rock*. The mystery crime series features a singer-songwriter protagonist trying to reclaim his glory days while solving murders in the fictional town of Libertyport, which looks a whole lot like Newburyport.

Within the pages of Brown's *Essex Coastal Byway Guide* the author shares the idiosyncrasies, landmarks, and beauty of the region.

Alan Bull (1964–)

Artist Alan Bull remembers feeling awestruck the first time he saw the Chain Bridge. As a young boy, he drove with his family south on Route 95 from their home in Old Town, Maine. He had no idea that this expanse between Newburyport and Amesbury, straddling the Merrimack River, would become a landmark in his own backyard when he moved to the Port in 1992—or that years later his infrastructure-inspired paintings would be featured in *Architectural Digest*. Kismet, talent, and Americana influence Bull's artistry.

His musician series, a collection of portraits of various musicians, allows Bull to blend his two passions. "In college, I had to decide between music or art school," he says. Bull is currently working on paintings of music legends to benefit the Elton John Aids Foundation (he presented Sir Elton with a piece of his artwork years back), and Bull has long supported many local charities with donations of his work. He also paints nudes, murals, monotypes, landscapes, and nautical scenes, and he teaches drawing and painting.

Bull is probably most well known for his truck series (which includes the painting *Rusty*, pictured on the opposite page). He traces its start to a rainy day in the mid-1990s when he painted a rendition of his grandfather's potato truck, using an old photograph of the auto relic, for the Newburyport Wet Paint auction. One potato truck eventually led to a 10-year retrospective exhibition of Bull's truck paintings at the Firehouse Center for Arts in 2006 and to his wildly received truck calendar series. He was again a featured solo artist at the Firehouse in 2014.

Speculating on the public's interest in his truck paintings, Bull says, "There's a certain beauty in the curves and the patinas of an old truck . . . it represents a living history, a part of Americana." Bull is simply happy to be a figure on the landscape he has come to love. "There's so much beauty here . . . the working waterfront, the buildings; it's difficult to put into words," says Bull. So he paints.

In 2012, Bull captured the beauty of Newburyport landmarks with a large wall mural that he painted on the wall of the Orange Leaf frozen yogurt shop in Market Square.

Dr. Carolyn Roy-Bornstein (1956–)

Author and pediatrician Carolyn Roy-Bornstein (pictured with her dog Homer) believes in the transformative power of words. Her memoir, *Crash: A Mother, A Son, and the Journey from Grief to Gratitude*, is a story of coping and healing after her son was gravely injured and his girlfriend killed by an underage drunk driver. The Newburyport High School teenagers had been walking along their street on a snowy evening when their world broke apart.

"Writing the book didn't feel very cathartic . . . it was more like picking scabs off of healing wounds," Roy-Bornstein says. Ultimately, however, putting her emotions into words allowed Roy-Bornstein to heal. It is the possibility of transformation that Roy-Bornstein hopes to share with others as editor of *Chicken Soup for the Soul—Recovering from Traumatic Brain Injury: Hope, Healing, and Hard Work*.

Harriet Prescott Spofford (1835–1921)

One of the most renowned authors of her era, Harriet Prescott Spofford broke the female stereotype: that of her own persona and that of fictional female characters she created.

Born in Calais, Maine, Miss Prescott moved to Newburyport with her family when she was 14 and began what would be a prolific writing life. Money earned from early articles and short stories she wrote helped support her family.

Prescott married Richard Spofford, a law partner of Caleb Cushing, when she was 30. The couple made their home on Deer Island, a small expanse of land between Newburyport's Chain Bridge and the town of Amesbury. The picturesque views nurtured Spofford's imagination.

Her Gothic short story "Circumstance" so impressed and unsettled Emily Dickinson that Dickinson said, "It followed me into the dark." (Courtesy of Elizabeth K. Halbeisen, University of Pennsylvania Press.)

Edith Heyck (1950–)

Born in Germany and raised in Maryland, expressionist artist Edith Heyck fell in love with the visual beauty of Newburyport during a visit here in the mid-1970s. Almost 40 years later, Heyck remains enchanted with her adopted hometown. Her stunning paintings of marshes and cityscapes capture the Port's mystique while revealing the artist's emotions.

"My aim is to reveal my rich inner world through design, color, and composition and to have the viewer share my experience," Heyck says.

She is also an accomplished graphic designer, but it's expressionism that captivates her muse. "Viewing my abstract paintings . . . evokes a response of the imagination, not the intellect," Heyck explains. Heyck's murals decorate many local landmarks, including the storefront window of New England Wine & Spirits and the Old Eastern Marsh Trail in neighboring Salisbury. Pictured above is Heyck's work of art titled *Storm Surge*. (Both, courtesy of Edith Heyck.)

Tom Ryan (1961–) and Atticus M. Finch (2002–)

Tom Ryan is the author of *Following Atticus*, a poignant memoir about how an unassuming miniature schnauzer, Atticus M. Finch, led a once overweight, out-of-shape newspaperman on a path of self-discovery through the humbling majesty of New Hampshire's White Mountains.

As Ryan fervently tells people, Atticus is not defined by breed; rather, the little dog is defined by his own spirit, heart, and individuality: "It's what has allowed Atticus to do so many things so many never thought possible for a little dog." But Atticus's greatest feat might be having had a paw—or all four—in gently nudging Ryan to achieve what he had never thought possible.

The intrepid duo moved from Newburyport to the White Mountains in 2007 after Ryan sold the weekly newspaper that he had founded, wrote, and edited. The *Undertoad* was part soapbox, part political journal, and always provocative. Ryan could be a scathing columnist, leaving some Newburyporters to question his integrity. But it was his humanitarian heart that Ryan followed as he and Atticus set out to scale 48 mountain peaks (each 4,000 feet) in 90 days—twice—during the winter. Inspired by a Newburyport friend who lost her battle with cancer, Ryan and Atticus's challenge became a humanitarian quest. With each ascent, they raised money to help find a cure for the disease. They also raised funds for Angell Memorial Medical Center, where veterinarians restored Atticus's sight after Ryan discovered his little dog had become blind; Ryan hadn't noticed at first because Atticus continued to lead the way on their hikes. Ryan and Atticus received the MSPCA-Angell Human Hero Award in 2008 during a ceremony at the John F. Kennedy Presidential Library and Museum.

Affectionately calling his friend "the little Buddha," Ryan says, "Atticus helped me to figure out what I am supposed to do with my life."

In May 2012, Ryan and Atticus welcomed into their lives a deaf, mostly blind, and ailing senior miniature schnauzer named Will. Ryan hadn't expected him to live long. But Will surprised Ryan. "He decided to love again, to be loved again, and to trust again," Ryan says. Since joining Ryan and Atticus, Will has walked forested trails and sat upon mountain peaks, ascending in the "Will wagon" that Ryan built. Ryan tells Will's remarkable journey in his forthcoming book. (Courtesy of Tom Ryan.)

Henry Coit Perkins (1804–1873)

Born inside the bygone Wolfe Tavern on State Street, Henry Coit Perkins was a medical doctor who opened his practice in downtown Newburyport in 1827. Regarded as "an intelligent gentleman," Perkins's interests included astronomy and meteorology, and he often lectured on these topics at the Newburyport Lyceum.

Fascinated by the latest scientific discoveries, Perkins is credited with being the first person in America to take a daguerreotype photograph.

Laura Coombs Hills (1859–1952)

Laura Coombs Hills was a Newburyport native and artist who rose to fame as a painter of miniature portraits. Her successful career earned her international awards. In her later years, Hills started painting floral pastels and received further acclaim. In 2012, the Laura Coombs Hills Gallery opened at the Newburyport Art Association, of which Hills was named an honorary founding member by portrait and landscape artist Sam Sargent. (Courtesy of the Historical Society of Old Newbury.)

Jay Schadler (1952–)

Two-time Emmy Award-winning journalist, photographer, and artist Jay Schadler called Plum Island home from 1989 to 2004. "I fell in love with Plum Island and its people," he says. It was from his Plum Island doorstep that Schadler began his hitchhiking adventure, crisscrossing America and interviewing everyday Americans in his travels for his ABC News Special, *Looking for America*.

Schadler continues to report for programs such as *20/20*, *World News*, and *Nightline* as well as networks like National Geographic and Discovery. These days, Schadler's true passion is his art: sublime collages he creates through photography and layered, chalked sketches. "I'm obsessed with the ability to take images and move them further forward," he explains. The solitary nature of his art, a contrast to the collaborative nature of his television reporting, appeals to him. Pictured below is his photograph titled *Essex Sandstone*. "Every story tells a picture," Schadler likes to say.

Dylan Metrano (1975–)

"Art is my life," Newburyport expatriate Dylan Metrano states. The songwriter, vocalist, and guitarist cofounded an alternative rock band while still in high school. Hamlet Idiot played to audiences throughout New England, releasing two albums and several singles on Chicago and New York record labels. Metrano received further acclaim as the frontman to Tiger Saw, the band he founded in 1999, distinguished by its textured, dreamy, and dark melodies.

Metrano has since become a lauded paper-cutting artist, displaying his artwork at several New England galleries. He describes his craft as a "meditative" experience. The whimsical cutouts he creates are reflective of the scenes and imagery of his native Newburyport and Monhegan Island, Maine, where Metrano spends his summers.

A self-described "art organizer," Metrano most enjoys showcasing a community's artists. Whether putting on theatrical productions or staging musical performances, Metrano intuitively plucks an eclectic blend of actors and musicians from his community to create scaled-back, intimate shows where performers and audience members meld through art.

Each December, Metrano returns to Newburyport to help organize an innovative "free art" show that he began with fellow artist Gordon Przybyla. He is one of about 30 artists who place their creations in bins throughout the city. People are encouraged to reach in and take a piece of donated art home with them. "It's the pure act of giving," says Metrano—words spoken from his artist's core.

Her Place in These Designs

The nude woman gracing the book cover of Rhina Espaillat's collection of poems *Her Place in These Designs* is a sculpture created by her husband, Alfred Moskowitz. It evokes a poignancy that is found within this poetic tome and within the tenderly melded relationship of Espaillat and Moskowitz.

In her poem, "On the Impossibility of Translation," Espaillat writes: "Yet lovers, each / mute in one skin, can learn to speak in tongues, / speak themselves whole."

Attuned to the nuances of language—and honored for her work in translations—Espaillat is also acutely attuned to the language of the heart.

Rhina Espaillat (1932–)

"Poetry leads you into your life," poet Rhina Espaillat declares. Born in the Dominican Republic, Espaillat has been captivated by the lyrical, honest nature of poetic verse ever since she was a girl. When she was seven years old, Espaillat and her family fled the dictatorship of Trujillo Molina and settled in New York City. Espaillat came to Newburyport in 1990 with her husband, Alfred Moskowitz.

She is the founder of the Powwow River Poets collective of Newburyport and a member of the musical poetry ensemble Melopoeia. Espaillat is the recipient of numerous literary prizes, including a Richard Wilbur Award, a T.S Eliot Prize, two Howard Nemerov Sonnet Awards, and a Robert Frost Foundation—Tree at my Window Award for translating Frost's poetry into Spanish. Espaillat is also a past honoree of the Newburyport Literary Festival.

Alfred Moskowitz (1925–)

Alfred Moskowitz is enchanted by the human form. Craggy faces, furrowed brows, folds and curves of the flesh inspire him. In each clay piece the sculptor creates, Moskowitz captures the humanity of his models.

Moskowitz has served as vice president and president of the Newburyport Art Association, where his collection of full-body and portrait sculptures was a featured exhibition. Moskowitz remains on the association's board of directors.

Douglas "Doug" Johnson (1944–)

Friendly Port personality Doug Johnson worked as a bartender at the legendary Grog for 40 years, retiring in 2013. The crooning vocalist-guitarist started the Sunday Night Blues Jam, which continues today with front man Parker Wheeler, whom Johnson hired.

These days, Johnson spends most of his time inside his bead bunker. The combination living space and studio is where the acclaimed bead artist strings together thousands of beads upon his loom to create intricate scenes of Newburyport and Plum Island.

One of Johnson's larger pieces of artwork depicts the Green Monster. His rendition of the fabled icon at Fenway Park, home to the world-champion Boston Red Sox baseball team, earned him an appearance on *Chronicle*, the New England-themed television program. Below is his bead-work piece titled "Blues Party."

Sam Sargent (1889–1959)

Led by a desire to cultivate art and restore a "cultural splendor" to his hometown of Newburyport, portrait and landscape painter Sam Sargent (pictured above), whose paintings have been exhibited worldwide, helped found the Newburyport Art Association in 1948. He served as the association's first president.

One of Sargent's portrait commissions was of Pres. Harry Truman in 1951. Civic-minded, Sargent served five years as a Newburyport city councilor. (Above, courtesy of the Newburyport Art Association; below, courtesy of Marge and Skip Motes.)

Joseph "Joe" Mannix (1936–)

The man who shares the moniker of a 1970s television detective worked for Newburyport's famed Towle Silversmiths as an office manager, became a self-employed accountant, and then became an unassuming real estate mogul before retiring at age 49—when he began exploring the world.

Mannix has ridden atop an elephant in Africa and a camel in Egypt, chatted with the Queen Mother when he visited London, fallen on the hood of the car carrying Princess Anne while visiting Prince Edward Island, met three popes, survived an attempted mugging in South America, and run along the Great Wall of China.

The native Newburyporter lives in his Plum Island villa, complete with miniature forest and sweeping views of Newburyport Harbor. From this locale, Mannix penned columns about island life for the former *Port Planet* and the original *Current*. (Left, courtesy of Joe Mannix.)

Bethany Groff (1974–)

"I love the moment when people figure out that history applies to and has resonance in their lives," says Bethany Groff. She believes that people's lives can become fuller and richer through an appreciation of history.

As the North Shore Regional Manager for Historic New England, Groff is entrusted with preserving 17th-century properties, including the Spencer-Peirce-Little Farm in Newbury. Col. Daniel Peirce, who in 1690 built the manor house (pictured below), is Groff's ancestor.

"I see a little bit of heritage everywhere," Groff says, "whether it's the name on a street sign in Newburyport . . . or here at Spencer-Peirce-Little Farm."

Her passion for historical preservation served as Groff's guide for writing *A Brief History of Old Newbury—From Settlement to Separation*. Her book captures the life and times—and scandal—of early Newbury and Newburyport.

Ghlee E. Woodworth (1958–)

One of the city's humble historians, Ghlee E. Woodworth says, "I'm just one of a long line of volunteers who have kept Newburyport's history alive." Genetics might have also played a role, because she is the daughter of late historian and community volunteer Todd C. Woodworth and longtime Red Cross volunteer Grace Jackson Woodworth. She is a 12th-generation descendant of Robert Adams, a first settler of the neighboring town of Newbury.

Through her previous service as a Peace Corps volunteer, Woodworth saw the world and helped humanity. She eventually became a mentor to the national staff of host countries and trained new volunteers for the organization, devoted to promoting world peace and friendship.

When Woodworth returned to Newburyport in 2005, in part to be with her aging parents, she took up her father's mantle as tour guide for his Tiptoe Through the Tombstones tours. "I was just a beginner," Woodworth recalls. "I didn't know a lot about Newburyport's history." However, as she discovered more about the legendary locals who lay beneath the marble and slate headstones of Oak Hill Cemetery, which date back to the early 1800s, she discovered that she shared her father's passion for historical research.

Woodworth's research led her to write *Tiptoe Through the Tombstones,* which details the lives and contributions of 80 Newburyporters who shaped the early years of the city. Published in 2009, the book won a number of awards and was a finalist for the American Association for State and Local History in 2010.

She has expanded her tombstone tours to include the city's other graveyards and its Underground Railroad, a network of escape routes and safe homes, facilitated by abolitionists and free blacks, to lead runaway slaves from the South to freedom.

Launched in 2013, Woodworth created an online series of self-guided history tours called the Clipper Heritage Trail. Residents, teachers, students, and visitors to Newburyport may download maps, brochures, historical profiles, and follow in the footsteps of legendary Newburyporters through 13 tours that cover the Clipper City. As to what her next project might be, Woodworth remarks, "As they say in the Peace Corps, some of the best projects are those you don't plan for." (Courtesy of Ghlee E. Woodworth.)

Mark Davis (1950–)

Award-winning documentary filmmaker Mark Davis captures the human experience of exploration: past, present, extraterrestrial, and internal.

He is perhaps best known for his Nova and National Geographic films depicting the Mars rover expeditions. *Mars Dead or Alive* (2004) tells the story of building and delivering the robotic rovers Spirit and Opportunity safely to Mars. *Welcome to Mars* (2005) follows the rovers' discoveries of water history on the Red Planet. The Emmy Award–winning *Five Years on Mars* (2008) chronicles the rovers' exploits over the first five years of a mission that was supposed to last just three months. *Death of a Mars Rover* (2011) bids farewell to Spirit, after the rover drove into a quicksand trap and went silent. And *Martian Mega Rover* (2012) documents the obstacle-fraught endeavor behind the new Curiosity rover and its climactic "Seven Minutes of Terror" landing drama.

"My goal is always to tell a compelling story," Davis states. "The Mars missions have a lot of inherent drama, and a lot of it happens on Earth. I always try to find the human dimension of a story. Machines are interesting, but people are fascinating, and high stakes situations often bring out the best in them."

Some of Davis's other documentaries explore a darker side of human nature. *Dinosaur Wars* (American Experience, 2011) chronicles the bitter rivalry between America's first dinosaur paleontologists, who fought for control of fossil fields in the American West after the Civil War. *Curse of T. Rex* (Nova, 1997), documents the fierce conflict between a commercial fossil dealer, scientists, a rancher, and the federal government over legal ownership of Sue, a nearly complete Tyrannosaurus rex skeleton discovered in South Dakota.

Private Lives of Dolphins (Nova, 1992), examines the complex social lives of these intelligent marine mammals, offering a glimpse into humans' evolutionary origins as social animals with large mammalian brains.

"I'm curious about the origins of things, the mysteries of the physical world, and the process of investigation," Davis explains, "whether it happens under water, in the desert, or on another planet."

"I also enjoy shaping a story. It's a bit like composing music, I think. If I had the talent, I'd do that instead. But I don't, so I'll stick to documentaries." (Courtesy of Mark Davis.)

Dennis Metrano (1942–)

Prior to coming to the Port, Dennis Metrano lived in Boston—inside a houseboat—atop a Back Bay brownstone. He wrote for the *Globe*, the *Herald*, and the *Phoenix* covering the entertainment beat and interviewing rock-and-roll legends such as David Bowie.

One day, Metrano drove north. He found himself inside the Grog, where he delightfully discovered the bar patrons to be writers, artists, and musicians—his kind of people. He relocated to Newburyport in 1978 and over the next decades established himself as a local journalist, founding the original *Current* and the *Port Planet*. Reflecting on the latter, penned with Metrano's stream-of-consciousness writing, he says, "It was exactly what I wanted it to be."

As a columnist for *Newburyport Today*, Metrano wrote as his alter ego, Muggsy Barnacle, dishing on friendly gossip. He came full circle when he resumed writing for the reincarnated *Current*.

Jane Niebling (1949–)

Jane Niebling cofounded the Newburyport Chamber Music Festival in 2002. As executive director, Niebling secures performance venues, finds local hosts for the artists, and handles everything behind the scenes.

Each summer, the festival commissions a world premiere of a never-before-performed instrumental piece. The local theme sometimes features a complementary text which Niebling previews. "I like to be involved in the creative aspect," she says. "Classical music is a living art . . . it's not only Mozart or Beethoven."

Niebling is also a print colorist. She hand-colors antique prints and maps, using styles and techniques reflective of a print's historical period. One piece she colored is a restrike edition of a Paul Revere print of the Boston massacre. When asked whether she feels a sense of interacting with history when she practices her craft, Niebling answers, "Absolutely."

Gordon Przybyla (1947–)

Buffalo, New York, native Gordon Przybyla only needed to experience the tranquility of the Parker River National Wildlife Refuge on Plum Island once to know that he wanted to live here. Przybyla unpacked his artist's muse in the Port in 1988; he still regards his surroundings with wonder. Pictured below is his work of art titled *Rich Spatial Flux.*

Today, Przybyla is a respected photographer, videographer, and abstract artist. He has contributed and photographed art installations at Maudslay State Park and photographed the carved coastline at Plum Island's Sandy Point. He has also created videos for local theater groups. Since 1988, Przybyla has led a life drawing group at Newburyport Art Association. Describing his fascination with the human form, Przybyla says, "Instead of worrying about creating an exact image, I use the figure as a starting point . . . to push paint around to convey a narrative."

Áine Greaney (1962–)

For novelist, essayist, and short story writer Áine Greaney, the craft of writing means to "practice a certain artist's generosity, a certain grace that transcends our own little lives and lines on a page." Each line of prose that Greaney writes is infused with her distinctive humanity.

Greaney's life began in County Mayo, Ireland, in a little village made famous for the filming of the 1952 movie classic *The Quiet Man*. She credits the rural and expansive countryside of her upbringing, with its "internal contours of isolation," in helping her to discover her writing voice.

"It's instinctive to me," Greaney says, "to place a fictional character in a geography or setting which either soothes or terrorizes him or her from the inside out." She writes with keen insight and compassion about an expansive, hauntingly beautiful, and tactile loneliness.

Greaney left Ireland in 1986, following a brief career as a primary school teacher, and landed in upstate New York. After earning a master's degree in English, Greaney enrolled in a fiction writing class where she "finally got the skills and courage to finish and publish a short story."

New York is also where she met Ken Ellrott, the "Yank" who would become her husband. The couple moved to Newburyport in 1999, where Greaney has been writing ever since.

Her short-story collection, *The Sheep Breeders Dance*, was followed by Greaney's debut novel, *The Big House*, set in her native Ireland. Her novel *Dance Lessons* a transatlantic story about three women and their intergenerational secrets, followed to critical acclaim. Among her writing awards and shortlists are the Hennessy Award for New Irish Writing, the Fish Anthology, the Rubery International Book Award, the Frank O'Connor Award, the Irish News Short Story Award, and Indie Lit 2011.

A featured author at the annual Newburyport Literary Festival, Greaney also teaches writing workshops at the Newburyport Art Association and at other locations throughout the region. Listening to Greaney speak might be just as enjoyable as reading her eloquent prose. She still speaks with a lilting Irish brogue, her green eyes sparkle with intelligence and mirth, and she likes to laugh. Ever authentic and true to her Irish heritage, Greaney knows how to bring the *craic*, an Irish term for fun.

Charlotte Vincent (1955–)
As layout designer, editor, and writer for the *Plum Island Pages*, Charlotte Vincent was happy to support this venture of her legendary late husband, Harry O'Connor, who served as publisher and editor.

"It was a unique community publication . . . to spread the news of this special place that Harry loved so dearly," says Vincent. The monthly newspaper ran from 1987 through 1994, the year O'Connor passed away. Working on the tribute issue "was a labor of love by all those who were a part of this special publication," Vincent recalls.

One special person was contributing writer Alex Hasapis, introduced to Charlotte and Harry by their friend and local newsman Dennis Metrano. Charlotte's friendship with Hasapis would grow and the two would eventually marry, each keeping in their hearts' cherished memories of "Harry O."

Frank/Fran Dalton (1928–2010) Frank Dalton migrated to Newburyport from Lawrence in the late 1960s, settling into the Port's gritty, bohemian artists' enclave. The freelance photographer focused his camera lens on his surroundings and captured scenes, and an epoch, of Newburyport.

Tall, lean, with craggy features and his silvery hair pulled back into a ponytail, Dalton himself was a portrait of virility. Except he did not feel that way. Dalton shared with friends that he felt his core was a female identity, yearning to be recognized as his true self.

Gradually, Frank evolved into Fran. As a transgendered individual, Fran kept her place as an artist in Newburyport's community, never shirking who she was. As Fran, Dalton wrote poetry and cultivated pumpkins; she created a totem to watch over her pumpkin patch.

Citizens remember Dalton's sensitivity not just for the artist's evocative photographs but for acts of kindness. It was Dalton who raised funds to erect a tombstone for Newburyport's legendary inebriated citizen Duncan Chase, replete with Chase's tag line, "I'm a cool, cool cat."

After Dalton died, journalist Victor Tine wrote a tribute column in the *Daily News of Newburyport* that beautifully captured the essence of the late artist and elicited an outpouring of affection. One reader responded, "As either Frank or Fran, here was a true artist, both of photography and of life itself. One of the most inspired, courageous, and noble people I have ever had the pleasure of knowing."

Pictured at the top of the opposite page is Fran Dalton in her pumpkin patch. At the bottom is "Pulling Contest," a photographic print by Fran Dalton. (All, courtesy of the Newburyport Archival Center at the NPL.)

Jean Foley Doyle (1929–)

"I never intended to be a writer," author Jean Foley Doyle shares. However, it was important to the lifelong Newburyporter, retired educator, and history scholar that the city have a record of its 20th century. So she wrote *Life in Newburyport*, two individual tomes that chronicle the life and times of the Port City from 1900–1950 and from 1950–1985, respectively.

Doyle approached her mammoth research task with humility and acumen. "No one else would do it . . . so I got stuck with it," she quips.

She is also an example of gumption and fortitude. The mother of 6 and grandmother of 11 earned her master's degree in history at age 42. When she was 80, while vacationing in Greece, Doyle suffered a broken neck. It took three years of intensive physical therapy, courage, and grit, but Doyle fully recovered. An avid gardener, Doyle traces her passion to her girlhood. "Each Sunday, my father would buy me a single flower," she remembers.

Not one to relax, Doyle advises, "Keep busy to enjoy life and always seek new opportunities to learn from people from all walks of life." In recognition of her life's work, the American Association for State and Local History presented Doyle, in 2012, with an Award of Merit for Leadership in History.

Rob Napier (1946–)

As a young boy, Rob Napier was left awestruck by the image of a model ship. Of his chosen vocation, the Newburyport model shipbuilder says, "I never seriously intended to be anything else."

His clients include the New York Yacht Club and institutions across the country. His maritime miniatures include half-models and full-hull, three-dimensional models. Before working on one of his exquisite pieces, Napier conducts extensive historical research.

He also repairs and restores models for exhibitions, working closely with conservators and curators. One of his major restoration pieces appears in the Art of Americas wing at Boston's Museum of Fine Arts, "a huge honor for me," says Napier.

A former US Navy journalist, Napier is the author of *Reconditioning an Eighteenth Century Ship— VALKENISSE—Retourschip of 1717*, which details his incredible effort in repairing a 300-year-old model of a Dutch ship.

I Remember,

I Remember

Poems by
CHRISTOPHER MICHAEL

Michael Ernest Lee "Christopher Michael" Stevens (1924–2007)
Christopher Michael was a kind and gentle soul who loved his adopted community of Newburyport, where he moved to in 1962. He was a poet, who at age 74 was named Newburyport's Poet Laureate in perpetuity.

Michael's poems, which he began writing at the age of four, poignantly capture his reflections on nature and the human condition. Always of delicate constitution—he suffered epileptic seizures as a child—Michael found power and solace in poetic verse.

His poetry collections include: *I Remember, I Remember*; *God Speaks to Me in All Religions*; and *A Deluge of Stars*, which includes the first poem he ever wrote, "Fireflies." After his wife predeceased him, Michael's constant companion became Amy, his devoted little dog. The two, one outfitted in flamboyant attire topped with a beret; the other roly-poly and lower to the ground, would often amble the streets late at night. "That's when the interesting people are out and about," Michael once said. When Amy passed, he adopted a feline companion from the Merrimack River Feline Rescue Society.

Organizers of the Newburyport Literary Festival honored Michael as a special guest at their 2007 event. The festival paid tribute to the humble man who served "as an example of creativity, optimism, the love of life and learning, and courageous independence in the face of adversity."

"He was barely able to walk but desperately wanted to be there," recalls venue host and Screening Room co-owner, Andrew Mungo, who, because Michael was too weak to recite, read one of Michael's poems on the poet's behalf.

When his frailness necessitated a wheelchair, Michael rolled himself the short distance from his apartment to Market Square, where he sat, watched, and held his poet's court. (Courtesy of the Newburyport Archival Center at the NPL.)

Nikole Beckwith (1980–)

Playwright, actor, comic artist, and rock musician Nikole Beckwith embraces each of her personas. Beckwith moved from Newburyport to New York City in 2006 to become an assistant to playwright-actor Eric Bogosian. It was her role as Sooze in Bogosian's play *subUrbia*, which Beckwith performed while a teenager at Newburyport's Firehouse Center for the Arts, that shaped her as a playwright and actor. "That play changed my life," she says. "It opened me up to what theater can be."

She is an alumnus of the New York–based Ensemble Studio Theatre's award-winning Youngblood, a collective of playwrights under the age of 30, and of the Public Theater's Emerging Writers Group. Beckwith's plays have been performed throughout New York City and at London's Old Vic theatre. Her first play, *Everything is Ours*, was a finalist for the 2011 National Playwrights Conference.

Stockholm, Pennsylvania, Beckwith's screenplay about "identity and family," earned her an Academy Nicholl Fellowship for Screenwriting in 2012. She was one of five chosen from 7,200 applicants. Beckwith was the first non-British playwright to receive a residency and opportunity to collaborate with the National Theatre Studio in London in 2013. While there, she wrote *Untitled Matriarch Play (or Seven Sisters)*, which received its world premier at London's Royal Court Theatre. Her comic strips highlight Beckwith's sardonic humor and have appeared in the *Huffington Post*.

Reflecting on her artistic development while growing up in Newburyport, Beckwith states, "I think that it was a perfect storm . . . a magical community of artists and people who were like-minded but also so different." People like legendary local Dylan Metrano, with whom she staged art shows. She also performed with Metrano's band, Tiger Saw, lending her vocals.

Beckwith teamed with legendary local Gregory Moss and his theater company, Independent Submarine, staging new and lesser-known plays and creating original work. "Greg is like my artistic soul mate; so much of the work we made together influences me to this day," she says.

As a teenager, she worked at the hip boutique Ganesh Imports, owned by legendary local Bill Bixby, whom Beckwith says, "is still often the first person to call and wish me a happy birthday."

"I grew up in a really amazing place," says Beckwith. (Courtesy of Nikole Beckwith.)

Gregory Moss (1976–)

"My childhood and adolescence in Newburyport formed my character," states acclaimed playwright, director, and thespian Gregory Moss. He was born in the Port after his parents moved here from Brooklyn, New York, when his father got a job teaching English at Newburyport High School.

Moss got his start with Theater in the Open at Maudslay State Park and later with the edgy former theater group Independent Submarine. Moss also credits "the street people and eccentrics who lived on the fringes of Newburyport society whom Moss says have had a "more lingering influence" upon his work, including "Drunken Duncan" (Duncan Chase), whose tag line was "I'm a cool, cool cat."

In an interview with the *Brooklyn Rail,* Moss said, "People who are caught between identities or caught between conventional modes of functioning, those are my people, those are my characters, people who can't quite fit into masculine or feminine roles I find engaging or empathic."

Moss's plays have been staged across the country, around the globe, and in his hometown of Newburyport at the Firehouse Center for the Arts and Theater in the Open. They include *House of Gold*, about the myth and image of murdered child beauty queen JonBenét Ramsey; *The Argument*, an apocalyptic fairy tale based on Hurricane Katrina, and *The Uses of Enchantment*, a contemporary fairy tale in the vein of the Brothers Grimm.

Moss explains that he is fascinated with fairy tales as story structures that "break the rules of realism to get at a kind of psychological or experiential realism." But he enjoys exploring other realms, too. As an example, *Punkplay*, is an "idiosyncratic genealogy of punk rock music" from 1980s America. These days, he travels more than he stays put, bringing theater to near and far-flung locales. He also teaches playwriting and screenwriting at the university level.

"I am itinerant," he says, "but I base myself mostly in New York—back in Brooklyn, where my family started." (Courtesy of Gregory Moss.)

CHAPTER SIX

Performing Artists

Newburyport is home to Theater in the Open, the Actors Studio of Newburyport, Exit Dance Theatre, and the Dance Place. The Firehouse Center for the Arts, which takes its name from the building's previous life as a firehouse, showcases cultural productions that include dance, theater, and an art gallery.

Anna Smulowitz is founder of Newburyport's Children's Theater, which morphed into Theater in the Open. Marc Clopton is a director-playwright-actor and founder of intimate theater known as the Actors Studio of Newburyport. Dancer-thespian Fontaine Dollas Dubus is owner of the Dance Place and artistic director of the modern dance company Exit Dance Theatre. Wire walker Ariele Ebacher, a Newburyport native now living in Chicago, is an alumnus of both Theater in the Open and the Dance Place.

Newburyport's musical heartbeat is the blues, at least on Sunday evenings when harmonica player Justin Quinn, who calls himself "an interpreter of the blues" hosts Sunday Soul evening at Glenn's Restaurant and Cool Bar. Just down the road, bluesman and harmonica player Parker Wheeler hosts his Blues Party at the Grog. The late Shirley Lewis, dubbed Regal Queen of the Blues, was a frequent Blues Party guest.

Flutist is only one of the musical identities of native Newburyporter Roger Ebacher. The self-trained musician most often associated with his flute playing is a composer and multi-instrumentalist. Guitarist John Curtis of the 1970s soft rock group Pousette-Dart Band makes his home in Newburyport. So does Tom Maginnis, drummer for the band Buffalo Tom, an alternative post-punk trio that he cofounded in 1986.

Newburyport native and retired Berklee College of Music professor and jazz drummer Les Harris Sr. has performed with jazz legends, including jazz trumpeter Herb Pomeroy. Classical guitarist John Tavano performs solo and with the poetic musical ensemble Melopoeia.

The above thespians and musicians, along with others from Newburyport's performing arts, are included in this chapter.

Les Harris Sr. (1932–)

Jazz drummer Les Harris Sr. has shared the limelight with jazz royalty including Willie "the Lion" Smith, Zoot Sims, and Dinah Washington.

After graduating from Newburyport High School in 1950, Harris joined the military. "My sole purpose for enlisting in the Navy," he shares, "was so I could attend the Navy School of Music." After his service to country, Harris enrolled in Berklee College of Music. While a student, he performed with Toshiko Akiyoshi and Anita O'Day as the house trio for Storyville in Boston's Copley Square. Closer to home, he gigged at Salisbury Beach. "I played the Edwards Hotel in the Down Below, also known as the Dugout. But I needed special permission from the owner because I was only 19," Harris shares. He reminisces about the almost nightly brawls that broke out and the quart-sized bottles of beer that went flying across the room. But he got to perform with jazz luminaries, including Herb Pomeroy.

During the 1970s, Harris brought the Count Basie Orchestra to Newburyport's annual Yankee Homecoming celebration. At another concert that Harris (pictured above and at left on the opposite page) organized, he performed with legendary big band drummer Gene Krupa (pictured at right on the opposite page). Harris also was the house drummer for many years at the former Sportsman's Lodge on the Plum Island Turnpike.

Harris ultimately returned to Berklee as a professor of music and taught there for 30 years. "My greatest reward was being given the opportunity to make a difference in the lives of my students," he says. It was not just Berklee students whom he helped. Through a music program he helped develop, Harris taught music theory at no charge to inner-city youth. The college presented Harris with an award acknowledging his selflessness.

Today, Harris teaches locally part-time, and he has been honored by the Newburyport Education Foundation for his artistic contribution to community. At a 2013 concert sponsored by Newburyport philanthropists Betsy and Jonathan Woodman, Harris performed with his son, Les Harris Jr., who is also a drummer and a music educator. Harris's granddaughter Aubrey, a bassist who shared the stage with country music star Keith Urban at the 2012 American Country Awards, accompanied her father and legendary grandfather.

"There's such a fine element of togetherness," Harris says, in describing what he calls "that jazz feeling" in performing with other musicians. As to the sound itself Harris adds, "It's like painting pictures with music." (Both, courtesy of Les Harris Jr.)

Justin Quinn (1951–)

Harmonica player Justin Quinn calls himself "an interpreter of the blues." The Newburyport musician performs and hosts the Sunday Soul evening at Glenn's Restaurant and Cool Bar, conversing with his audience through his musical instrument.

Quinn first picked up the harmonica as a high school student. While playing along with a song on the radio in what he describes as an "altered state of mind," Quinn experienced an epiphany. "This is what I want to do," Quinn recalls feeling.

He had careers as a chef and hairdresser, but his lifeblood has always been music—the blues that pulsate through his veins.

"Everyone can relate to the blues," says Quinn, who played pre-war blues with the band Roll & Tumble prior to taking over the blues pulpit at Glenn's.

Zach Field (1978–)

Zach Field, owner of Zach Field Drum Studios and, since 2014, owner of the Musical Suite (each located in the Tannery Marketplace), has been drumming since the age of four.

In teaching others the art of percussion, Field says his greatest reward is witnessing his students experience a breakthrough moment when, through the vibration created by their drumming, they tap into something deeper within themselves. "Their faces will light up," Field says.

Vibration is the emphasis of Field's side vocation, the Gong Meditation Project. He explains that when used meditatively, a gong's peal can "loosen up" the mind.

Founder of the Plum Island Steel Drum Band, Field performs throughout the region. In 2013, his band performed at a world premiere for the Newburyport Chamber Music Festival. An athlete, Field tests his mettle in national triathlons.

Anna Smulowitz (1947–)

Anna Smulowitz, who jokingly refers to herself as a "wandering Jewish Theater," moved to Newburyport in 1979. Shortly thereafter, she founded the Newburyport Children's Theater featuring the city's young thespians.

Smulowitz fondly recalls her creative promotion of *African Folk Tales*, her first production. "I wanted a fun way to get the word out about the play, so I put on an African headdress and walked through downtown, beating a drum." Twenty years later, with the children's theater having morphed into Theater in the Open, Smulowitz again donned costume and paraded through town, along with her cast of actors, to promote the 1999 musical production *Peter Pan*. She has acted in, directed, or produced more than 100 plays and mentored over 1,000 students, many of whom became film, theater, and television actors. Shakespeare, the Brothers Grimm, Theresa Linnihan (a former director of Newburyport Children's Theater), and Arthur Miller are just a few of the playwrights and bards whose works she has showcased at venues throughout Newburyport, including Maudsley State Park, the Actor's Studio of Newburyport at the Tannery Marketplace, and the Firehouse Center for the Arts.

She has staged her own play, *Terezin, Children of the Holocaust,* in Newburyport, across the country, and abroad, including performances at Terezin and Germany's Auschwitz Museum. The play holds deep, personal meaning for Smulowitz; her parents met as prisoners at Auschwitz, the notorious concentration camp. Smulowitz was later born in a displaced persons camp. A poignant and profound Holocaust drama, the play's title refers to the child prisoners inside the walls of the Nazi propaganda creation, Terezin. With its paradise facade—intended to deny to the world the horrors and atrocities that the Nazis were committing against humanity—Terezin was, in reality, a stopover for children before they were sent to Auschwitz.

Audiences are always moved to emotion by the play's intensity, but perhaps no two audience members have been more touched than Smulowitz's parents. "They were very proud of me and impressed that I listened to their stories," says Smulowitz.

Listening is something Smulowitz practices in her other role as an ordained, interfaith chaplain. "I try to be a listening presence," she says.

Danny Harrington (1952–)

Saxophonist Danny Harrington believes that each instrument has its own personality and that a musician's job is to coax from each instrument its "unique musical timbre." If the relationship between musician and instrument is good, the personality of the instrument—and soul of the musician—will be bared.

Harrington's "hey day," as he calls it, was during the early 1990s, when he toured with the Tommy Dorsey Orchestra and performed with legendary musical luminaries such as the Four Tops, the Temptations, Diana Ross, and Gladys Knight. He recalls a personable Knight who warmly greeted and introduced herself to Harrington, a memory with a lasting musical imprint.

The person whom Harrington credits with helping him develop as a musician is jazz music's elder statesman, clarinet and saxophone player Teddy Casher. "It was 1974 and I was playing the Providence bar scene; through an acquaintance, I met Casher, who happened to hear me on the bari sax," says Harrington. (At the time, Harrington considered himself to be more of an alto or tenor sax player.) After his performance, Harrington says that Casher told him, "I hate to tell you this, but you're a baritone saxophone player." Harrington jokes that the baritone saxophone has a small image problem—but somehow, Harrington has been able to make this imposing, low-pitched woodwind resonate with the reverberations of soulful jazz. He praises Casher for giving him "the strength to keep at it" and calls Casher his "musical father."

For Harrington, the pull of the deep bass lines of his bari sax is matched by the pull of the community where he lives. He has been a citizen of Newburyport for more than 20 years, having served 11 years on the board of directors for the Firehouse Center for the Arts—three of those years as president. "How could I not get involved?" he asks retrospectively. Harrington says he wanted to help bring arts to the community that "kept calling to him." His recording *Danny Harrington—Live at the Firehouse Theatre* was made there in 2001. Harrington's first recording is *Risa's Waltz*, a composition that he wrote for his wife in 1990. He coaxed the melody from his musician's soul.

Joe Holaday (1957–)

"I'm a bass player, heart and soul," says Joe Holaday, whose impressive music resume includes the role of bassist for the parody-loving, bombastically fun Boston party band the Fools and the popular Beatles tribute band Beatlejuice.

He asserts that being a bass player is the best job in a band. "You're in the catbird seat," Holaday says. "You're the fulcrum for where the melody and harmony come together." Holaday jokes that whereas the lead singer and guitarist are a band's "super heroes," the bass player is the lieutenant on the battlefield who deftly goes about his work largely unnoticed but whose contributions have a distinct impact. "That's a beautiful thing," says Holaday.

But it was Holaday's culinary expertise that brought the Topsfield, Massachusetts, native to Newburyport in 1979. He had been working as an overnight grill cook at the bygone Howard Johnson's restaurant on Route 1 when Steve Farrell, then co-owner of Ten Center Street, popped in and had Holaday grill him a piece of halibut. Farrell was so impressed that he offered Holaday a job at his Newburyport restaurant.

During his 13 years at Ten Center Street, Holaday honed his culinary skills. He also met his wife, Donna, then a bartender at the restaurant who would become the first mayor of Newburyport elected to a four-year term.

All the while, Holaday was playing in various bands. The Fools came calling in 1982 when their original bass player left. However, Holaday had decided that his trajectory was in the culinary realm. Although he initially turned down the Fools's offer, he agreed to sit in for an upcoming gig.

"It was transforming, having all these people pressed against the stage, singing the words to the songs and dancing," Holaday remembers. He was hooked. Holaday stayed with the Fools until 2007, but he still plays the occasional show. These days he's passionate about Beatlejuice. The band is a favorite of Newburyport's Yankee Homecoming concert series. "It's so great to look out into the crowd and see three generations of families, singing, dancing, and having fun," says Holaday.

Reflecting both upon his culinary history and his musicianship, Holaday says, "With cheffing, you are training your palate to discern different flavors. With music, you are training your ear to hear different tones." Each, he asserts, is about creating harmony. "I'm really lucky," Holaday says of his harmonious life. (Courtesy of Joe Holaday.)

Roger Ebacher (1952–)

"I consider myself very fortunate . . . I've been able to develop my career in the town where I grew up," composer and multi-instrumentalist Roger Ebacher reflects on his musical development in his hometown of Newburyport.

The self-trained musician is most often associated with his flute playing, but flutist is only one of Ebacher's identities. Describing himself as "a participant in today's rapidly evolving musical universe," Ebacher has immersed himself over the past three decades in a variety of musical genres, from folk, pop, blues, funk, and jazz, to world music.

Ebacher began performing professionally while attending Concordia University in Montreal, where he majored in literature and poetry. He played the flute, piano, and sang in the downtown clubs of the city that first infused his jazz soul. "This was 1971, before the advent of the Montreal International Jazz Festival," Ebacher refers to the annual event, which draws "jazz pilgrims" from across the globe. (Ebacher visited the Jazz Festival for the first time in 2005 and was "blown away" by the talent.)

Returning to Newburyport after college, Ebacher "fell head-first into jazz" when he joined the Charles Belcher Group. He describes the band as having been the "closest living thing to Thelonious Monk in New England."

He went on to play in Timestream, the seven-piece "seminal punk-jazz band" of the late 1970s. Touring New England, Ebacher says, "We blew the roof off every venue we visited." Along the way, Ebacher composed musical scores for theater productions. He also made his acting debut in community theater. But Ebacher quickly returned to his first passion: creating music. He began performing under his own name, with guest appearances on the recordings of other New England artists.

Pulling together a quartet of likewise talented musicians, Ebacher made his first recording as a bandleader, releasing *Flutation Device* in 1998. Under the Roger Ebacher Quintet, he released *Backyard Carneval* in 2001. Ebacher describes the sound as "Afro-Cuban/Brazilian–Latin jazz."

The influence of world music is evident in Ebacher's current project, *The Air Department*. "It's an accurate reflection of where I am now as an artist, and that sense of artistic fulfillment is something that I am deeply thankful for," Ebacher states. (Courtesy of Alison Ebacher Photography.)

John "Johnny" Battis (1937–2011)

Newburyport jazz clarinet player Johnny Battis (pictured fourth from the left) had an excellent time in life. Fittingly, one of the bands he played in was called the Excellent Jazz Band led by his friend and bandmate Dick Kaplan (pictured third from the left). A multi-instrumentalist, he played in a string of other ensembles throughout his musical career.

The Boston Conservatory of Music alumnus graduated first in his class and served as a Newburyport city councilor. When neighbors complained about a derelict lot overgrown with weeds and littered with debris, Battis single-handedly transformed an eyesore into a bucolic respite. Today, Battis Grove Park is the entrance to Newburyport's Clipper City Rail Trail. Thoughtful, kind, and sentimental, Battis baked cookies for his neighbors every Christmas; after snowstorms, he shoveled out the shelters of feral cats who lived in sterilized colonies along the waterfront, and each year he placed flowers on the grave of writer J.P. Marquand. (Above, courtesy of Theresa Battis.)

Fontaine Dollas Dubus (1962–)

Lifelong dancer Fontaine Dollas Dubus is owner of the Dance Place and artistic director of the modern dance company Exit Dance Theatre, each located in the city's Tannery Marketplace.

She has performed in numerous productions. One of her greatest rewards, however, is teaching her students to release the dance that resides inside their own bodies.

In addition to being a dancer, Dubus is a passionate advocate for women's rights. "I am a feminist," she clearly asserts. She's also a thespian. Dubus has given scripted readings for the *Vagina Monologues* and for Mark Twain's *The Diaries of Adam and Eve.*

On Valentine's Day 2013, the opportunity to blend her passion for dance with her women's advocacy presented itself. Asked to participate in an event for One Billion Rising, a worldwide anti-violence movement, Dubus says, "I jumped at the chance." She organized a flash mob of more than 100 dancers who moved their bodies in synchronized rhythm, raising funds and awareness for women's issues.

Expressing herself through dance is intrinsic to her soul. "I feel that I am most myself when I am dancing," Dubus says. "Dance is in my body. I couldn't live without it."

Ariele Ebacher (1978–)
An alumnus of Theatre in the Open and the Dance Place, Ariele Ebacher has always loved to perform. So when the traveling troupe Circus Smirkus came to the Port in 1997, Ebacher fell under the circus spell. Two years later, she joined the young group of performing artists—first as a stage manager and counselor before she was introduced to her true passion: the art of wire walking.

Now an accomplished low wire walker, Ebacher dazzles and awes audiences around the globe with her ballerina grace and athletic precision in thrilling and deftly choreographed performances. The veteran artist still finds wire walking exciting. "What still gives me goose bumps is feeling that I have really touched an audience, that they have been truly affected by the experience we have created and shared together," Ebacher says. When she's not touring, Ebacher teaches wire walking and other circus skills. Her home base is Chicago.

"My knowledge and experience of the world have always been through the performing arts," says Ebacher. "I do it because the world needs the performing arts as a place where people share a live experience that can reach beyond the material world and into the realms of dreams, emotion, and imagination." (Photograph by Jim Newberry; courtesy of Ariele Ebacher.)

Liz Frame (1960–)

Musical artist Liz Frame believes that if people listen to their true selves they can find their paths to happiness. Listening to Frame perform with her band, the Kickers, can help. The songwriter, vocalist, and guitarist reminds audiences that life is meant to be enjoyed. As she releases each note, Frame delivers songs that are full of mettle and promise. Her seasoned voice empathizes with "the human condition," reverberating through her listeners' cores.

"I am moved by people's stories," says Frame. "I admire those who, by becoming more self-aware, overcome obstacles."

Frame began writing songs as a young girl; her distinctive vocals have drawn comparisons to k.d. lang, Lucinda Williams, and the Indigo Girls. A presence on greater Newburyport's music scene, Frame and her band toured the Mid-Atlantic states in 2013 following the acclaim of their record, *Sooner*. (Courtesy of Liz Frame.)

John Ryan "J.R." Gallagher (1980–)

"Newburyport is a special city, even amongst other coastal cities," says J.R. Gallagher. "Cool stuff goes on here; we have eccentric characters, a unique history, beautiful scenery . . . it just doesn't get much better than this."

A guitarist, Gallagher shares that one of his coolest experiences was performing a live soundtrack with his former band Tiger Saw to the vampire film *Nosferatu* at the Screening Room. Gallagher possesses a playful irreverence balanced by a humanitarian heart. He serves on the board of directors for I.C. Haiti, founded by parishioners of Newburyport's Immaculate Conception Church to provide health care and education to Haiti's poor. In a poignant encounter, Gallagher met the children helped by his organization when he visited in 2010, months after a catastrophic earthquake hit the impoverished nation. (Courtesy of Meg Manion Photography.)

John Tavano (1951–)

Classical guitarist John Tavano's musical repertoire includes flamenco, Brazilian, Latin, Cuban, bossa nova, and jazz. He explains that textured phrasing, when evoked through a guitar, has the power to suggest imagery that personally resonates with listeners. Tavano describes the guitar as a "poetic instrument with a consoling influence."

In the poetic musical ensemble Melopoeia, Tavano allows the voice of his guitar to accent the lyrical quality of verse. Poet Alfred Nicol says, "John can pick something out of his pocket from two centuries ago and match, syllable for syllable, the poetic verse."

Tavano also teaches, demonstrating to his students the romantic nature of the classical guitar along with performing techniques and historical significance.

His performance band, the Latin Quarter, is a shape-shifting ensemble of gifted fellow musicians who create sensuous dance music.

John Curtis (1950–)
Guitarist for the 1970s soft rock group Pousette-Dart Band (PDB), John Curtis recalls opening for Yes, Peter Frampton, Little Feat, Jimmy Buffet, and, he says, "a bunch more that I can't remember." Call it "Amnesia," as in the band's 1977 hit song and album, which found a place on the Billboard Top 200.

PDB broke up in 1981 but has performed multiple reunion shows over the years, including a 2007 acoustic show at Newburyport's Firehouse Center for the Arts. Curtis's first Newburyport visit was to the Grog in 1969. "It was pretty rough back then with sawdust on the plywood floor," Curtis says of the legendary Newburyport landmark. He moved from Somerville to Newburyport in 1985 and later open Curtis Studio, where today Curtis teaches acoustic and electric guitar, mandolin, banjo, ukulele, and bass guitar. (Below, courtesy of John Curtis.)

John Curtis   John Troy   Jeffrey Teague   Jon Pousette-Dart

POUSETTE-DART BAND

Tom Maginnis (1965–)

Tom Maginnis is fascinated by the "intersection of genius and madness and art." He shared this observation in a 2011 interview with *Magnet* magazine during a discussion about legendary jazz pianist Thelonious Monk. With regard to his own artist profile, Maginnis says, "I hope there's a tiny bit of genius in the madness."

Maginnis is the drummer for Buffalo Tom, the alternative post-punk trio that he cofounded in 1986 with vocalist and guitarist Bill Janovitz and bassist Chris Colbourn while the three were students at UMass Amherst. (The band's name is the result of tomfoolery, wordplay that stuck.) They released their first album in 1988, the self-titled *Buffalo Tom*.

"Sodajerk," a song from the trio's 1993 *Big Red Letter Day*, was featured on the soundtrack for the television series *My So-Called Life*; the band also appeared in an episode. They were the featured musical guests on *The Jon Stewart Show*.

Buffalo Tom garnered critical acclaim and an international fan base during its pinnacle years of the late 1980s through mid-1990s. It was during this period that Maginnis, a native of Andover, Massachusetts, settled in Newburyport with his wife, a graphic designer.

Maginnis jokes that he blazed a trail for stay-at-home dads, escorting his two little girls (now young women) to the Inn Street Playground each day while Buffalo Tom stepped out of the spotlight for nearly a decade to focus on family life. Although the band never broke up, Maginnis teases that if there had been a scandal in their history, a "reunion" record might reap more mainstream attention. Nevertheless, their 2011 release, *Skins*, was received with honest praise.

As drummer for the Newburyport-based, dad-formed band *Das Pintos*—Maginnis's other musical project—he says that getting people to dance is behind "the madness."

A glimpse through the prism of Maginnis's life reveals intersecting and enduring relationships—a melding of music, family, friends, and community—cultivated and artfully preserved with a "tiny bit of genius."

Shirley Lewis (1937–2013)

"Regal Queen of the Blues" Shirley Lewis lived in Newburyport during the late 1980s to mid-1990s. The captivating soul singer with the big voice, big heart, and penchant for colorful robes and unusual hats quickly cultivated a legion of friends and fans.

"She was a grand performer," says bluesman Parker Wheeler, founder of the weekly Blues Party at the Grog. "It was always a great time when Shirley came to town." Even after Lewis left the Port, she returned regularly to join Parker on stage.

Joe Laite, Lewis's next-door neighbor, close friend, and founder of the Newburyport Bluescruise says of the regal blues queen, "[Shirley] had a magnetic quality that allowed her to make friends very quickly. She also was warm and had a genuine demeanor and spirit, as well as being very humble, grateful, and spiritually aware." Laite fondly recalls playing in the informal blues jams held inside Lewis's High Street apartment. Lewis would become a favorite performer on Laite's Bluescruises.

During her six-decade career, Lewis performed with B.B. King, Ike and Tina Turner, Wilson Pickett, and Ray Charles. She received the Boston Blues Legend Award, the Blues Trust Lifetime Achievement Award, and many other achievement awards. Newburyport Mayor Donna Holaday proclaimed September 21, 2013, Shirley Lewis Day. Holaday read an official Massachusetts State House proclamation and added Newburyport's own endorsement and heart-felt sentiments while aboard the Shirley Lewis Memorial Bluescruise on that day. The cruise celebrated Lewis's life and benefited the Living the Blues Foundation. Created in honor of the Regal Queen of the Blues, the foundation continues Lewis's legacy and acts of humanity by raising money for women's crisis centers and providing an annual blues scholarship.

Her adult daughters, Angela and Joy, remember the love their mother showered upon them. "We were her greatest joy in life," says Angela. "But music was a close second, always. 'Mommy' loved singing; it was her gift from God to share with the world, to touch people. Singing also helped mom give her girls a better life, and a better life is what we both have today." (Courtesy of James T. Kenney.)

Marc Clopton (1951–)

Marc Clopton is thrilled to call the 50-seat black box theater known as the Actors Studio of Newburyport, located in the Tannery Marketplace, home. The director, playwright, actor, and former Los Angelean (by way of Washington, DC,) unpacked his bags and his artist's muse in Newburyport in 1991; he began teaching acting classes shortly thereafter.

With a mission to "encourage full creative expression and develop the art form and the individual," Clopton helps actors discover and share their souls with audiences. For the Actors Studio's 20th anniversary celebration in 2011, Clopton staged a collection of 14 plays that he wrote himself. Titled *Marc's Shorts*, Clopton humorously posed, holding a pair of boxer shorts, in a poster advertising the debut of his short mini-dramas. He staged *Marcs Shorts 11* in 2013.

A practicing shaman for 24 years, Clopton is fascinated by the interplay between the conscious mind and the unconscious mind. He's led full-moon ceremonies where participants, gathered in a circle, share personal declarations—each baring witness to and supporting one other.

Clopton's shamanistic perspective led him to support his friend and fellow Actors Studio board member Julie McConchie as they created the community-based photographic event, "Dear World/Dear Newburyport" in 2013. The original "Dear World" project began in New Orleans, following Hurricane Katrina. Survivors used their bodies as canvasses, upon which they wrote love notes to their city. The Newburyport project stayed true to the original. Participants were invited to give full expression to their true selves by writing personal messages to the Port City upon their legs, arms, faces, and feet. Each person was then photographed by Robert X. Fogarty, creator of the New Orleans event, who had traveled to the Port. The poignant portrait presentation was unveiled at a reception held at city hall.

Clopton says the citywide event was intended to inspire deep and meaningful conversation about what matters most to each of us, as individuals and as a community. His two personal messages: "Love & Laughter" and "It's YOUniversal."

"I was supposed to become an architect," Clopton reveals. But while a student at the University of Maryland, "quirks of fate" led him to the theater department. One day he found himself backstage, watching actors interact with one another. "They were all glowing," he recalls. "I knew then what I wanted to do with my life."

Sitting inside the dark and magical space of the Actors Studio of Newburyport, Clopton glows.

Parker Wheeler (1947–)

Since 1990, bluesman Parker Wheeler has been packing the Grog's cabaret on Sunday evenings for his Blues Party. The loyal legions of fans come for the music, the camaraderie, and they come to dance.

Each week, the veteran harmonica player shares the stage with a stellar core of supporting musicians and a featured musical guest or two. One of Wheeler's first guest luminaries was Matt "Guitar" Murphy. Wheeler discovered the blues was his passion and the harmonica his instrument at age 18, playing along to Muddy Waters records. "I learned early: don't try to tell everything you know in one song," he says.

As host of what he lovingly refers to as the "longest running and cheapest group therapy session," Wheeler—the consummate performer—asserts, "It's absolutely still a thrill for me each week." (Courtesy of LaVerne Wheeler.)

BIBLIOGRAPHY

Bierfelt, Kristin. *The North Shore Literary Trail*. Charleston, SC: The History Press, 2009.

Doyle, Jean Foley. *Life in Newburyport: 1900–1950*. Portsmouth, NH: Peter E. Randall Publisher LLC, 2007.

———. *Life in Newburyport: 1950–1985*. Portsmouth, NH: Jetty House, an imprint of Peter E. Randall Publisher, 2010.

Hill, Sarah J. and Harry B. Jr. *Yankee City . . . Faces from our Past*. Newburyport, MA: Courtesy of The Newburyport Five Cents Savings Bank, 2001.

Woodworth, Ghlee E. *Tiptoe Through the Tombstones, Oak Hill Cemetery, Volume 1*. Newburyport, MA: The Journeyman Press, 2008.

Wright, John Hardy. *Images of America: Newburyport*. Charleston, SC: Arcadia Publishing, 1999.

INDEX

AN IMPRINT OF ARCADIA PUBLISHING

Find more books like this at
www.legendarylocals.com

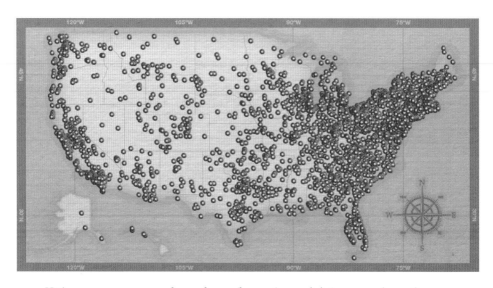

Discover more local and regional history books at
www.arcadiapublishing.com